PROJECT MANAGEMENT

IN HEALTH AND

COMMUNITY SERVICES

Getting good ideas to work

3rd Edition

Judith Dwyer, Zhanming Liang
and Valerie Thiessen

Routledge
Taylor & Francis Group

LONDON AND NEW YORK

First published 2004 by Allen & Unwin

Published 2020 by Routledge
2 Park Square, Milton Park, Abingdon, Oxon OX14 4RN
605 Third Avenue, New York, NY 10017

First issued in hardback 2021

Routledge is an imprint of the Taylor & Francis Group, an informa business

 A catalogue record for this book is available from the National Library of Australia

Internal design by Romina Panetta
Index by Puddingburn
Set in 11.5/14 pt Bembo by Midland Typesetters, Australia

ISBN 13: 978-0-367-71910-4 (hbk)
ISBN 13: 978-1-76063-281-6 (pbk)

Contents

Glossary of terms

80-hour rule A rough guideline about the normal scale of activities in a work breakdown structure: no single activity should require more than 80 hours (or two weeks) of work.

Activities A collection of related tasks that contribute to a single deliverable.

Agile CA system or software development method.

Benefits A net positive change in outcomes, including patient care and health or wellbeing outcomes.

Benefits realisation A method of evaluating project success according to whether the intended benefits (financial or other) are achieved, often some time after the project itself is completed. Used most frequently in information systems projects.

Best practice A method or technique that has consistently shown results superior to those achieved with other means and that may be used as a benchmark.

Budget A financial document that forecasts or plans the expected dollar inflows (revenue) and dollar outflows (expenses) for a project.

Business case A document that describes an intended service or 'business' in operational and financial terms, and seeks to establish that the service as planned can be financially viable (or profit-able)—a positive business case is one in which the revenue/benefits outweigh the costs.

Buy-in The level of support among any group of stakeholders (often staff and management) for the project and/or the proposed changes.

Cash flow The movement of money into and out of a business, project or financial entity during a specified period of time.

Close/close-out   The fourth phase of the project cycle, when the process of handover, or transitioning from the project to the new method or state, is completed.

Commissioning   This term has two meanings:
1. The process of ensuring that a new facility, piece of equipment or service is fully operational.
2. The process of engaging a team, company or consultant to conduct a project, service or other activity on behalf of the funding agency.

Contingency   A potential problem or change in the project; an amount of money or other resource held within the project to cover elements of risk or uncertainty.

Control   Ensuring that the project keeps to the agreed project scope, budget, schedule and quality.

Cost-benefit analysis (CBA)   Estimates (in monetary terms) the costs and benefits (or measure of effect) of an intervention or program.

Cost-effectiveness analysis (CEA)   Compares relative cost and outcomes (or effect) of two or more interventions with the effect expressed in non–monetary terms using 'natural units' such as cure rate or reduction in the incidence of a disease.

Cost-utility analysis (CUA)   Expresses outcomes in the non–monetary unit of quality-adjusted life years (QALYs) so that comparisons of benefit can be made between alternative treatments or interventions.

Critical success factors (CSF)   The important aspects of projects (and their contexts) that are known to affect the achievement of outcomes.

Deliverable leg   A graphical presentation in a WBS of the work required to complete each deliverable.

Deliverables   The concrete goods or services that will be produced by the project and handed over on its completion.

Direct costs   The costs incurred by and for the project that would not otherwise be incurred by the organisation.

Economic evaluation   Type of analysis that estimates the relative value of alternative options.

Effectiveness   The extent to which planned outcomes are achieved by a service or product in normal conditions (rather than in the laboratory or in trials). The answer to the question 'does it work in practice?'

Efficacy   The extent to which planned outcomes are achieved by a service or product in ideal conditions. The answer to the question 'can it work?'.

Electronic Health Record (EHR) or Electronic Medical Record (EMR)   The systematised collection of patient and population health information, electronically stored in a digital format.

Escalate   Taking problems or issue/s higher in the organisation in order for them to be resolved, or implementing the next level of action required to overcome an identified risk.

Evaluation indicators   Markers of a project's progress, change and success.

Evidence-based practice   Decisions in (clinical) practice based on evidence from research studies and other sources of reliable information (for example, internal data).

Exclusions   What is out of the project scope (what the project won't do).

Expenditure items   Expenses incurred by a project.

Feasibility study   A process that objectively and rationally examines whether a proposed project, service or system can be successfully implemented.

Gantt chart   A commonly used method of presenting the timelines and tasks of a project, and of charting actual progress. It plots activities (in rows) against the timeline (in columns), thus showing the relationships between them.

Gap analysis   An assessment of information about gaps and potential capacity in the available service system.

Gateway Review/Process   A project assurance methodology to improve the delivery of major projects. It involves short, sharp and confidential reviews conducted by reviewers not associated with the project at six key stages of the project life cycle, also known as 'gates'.

Go/no go   The time at which the organisation decides whether or not to proceed with the next stage of a project, or to accept a chosen system or model.

Go-live   The time at which a product, deliverable or outcome is put into practice.

Goal   A statement of what the project aims to achieve.

Grey literature   Research that is unpublished or not published in the peer-reviewed research literature, such as government reports and policy documents.

Impact evaluation Measures achievement of the project's goals and objectives—that is, it focuses on the short-term results.

Implementation Planning Study (IPS) A study conducted prior to ICT or information-system implementation to understand the solution to be implemented, the requirements of the implementing agency, and confirm the implementation scope and approach.

Information and Communications Technology All devices, networking components, applications and systems that in combination allow people and organisations to interact in the digital world.

In-kind funding Resources (other than money) that are provided to enable or support a project, such as staff time, office space and administrative support.

Indirect costs Costs incurred that are not readily identified and attributed to a particular project. These costs may be necessary for the implementation and completion of the project, but are 'built in' or shared with other activities within the organisation.

Investment Logic Map A simple single-page flow chart that tells the story of an investment and exposes its underpinning logic.

Labour Budgeted costs for staff required to do the work of the project, both those employed by the organisation and external contractors.

Lean thinking An approach to business processes (or processes of care) that aims to create more value (for patients, clients or customers) while minimising resource waste (cost, time, errors and rework).

Lessons learned log Project lessons learned should be captured and placed in a log that will be available to the project management team.

Literature review (see also Systematic literature review) A process of finding, describing, summarising, evaluating and clarifying evidence found in the literature.

Monitor Conduct regular review and reporting of the project progress.

Needs assessment or needs analysis An activity to develop a comprehensive understanding of a problem or need in the community or population, in order to identify interventions or strategies that can solve that problem or address that need.

Objectives Statements of the steps or changes that need to be achieved in order to achieve the goal.

Outcome evaluation Measures the longer-term achievements or results of the project.

Pilot study A small-scale preliminary study conducted in order to evaluate feasibility, time, cost and adverse events, and to improve upon the study design prior to performance of a full-scale project.

Post-Implementation Review (PIR) Conducted after completing a project to evaluate whether project objectives were met, to determine how effectively the project was run, to learn lessons for the future, and to ensure that the organisation gets the greatest possible benefit from the project.

Probity (tender process integrity) A tendering process that is fair, impartial, transparent, secure, confidential and compliant with legislative obligations and government policy.

Process evaluation Measures the effectiveness of the strategies and methods used in the project, and the skill of their execution.

Procurement Deals with the sourcing activities, negotiation and strategic selection of goods and services that are usually of importance to an organisation.

Program A group of projects managed in a coordinated way, or a service, intervention or set of activities that aims to meet a health or social care need.

Program evaluation and review technique (PERT) A statistical tool for scheduling projects that specifies and analyses the tasks involved and significant milestones.

Program logic A method of planning and evaluating projects that specifies the links between the goals of a service or project and the inputs, processes, outputs and impacts/outcomes it will produce to achieve those goals.

Project assurance A discipline that seeks to provide an independent and objective oversight of the likely future performance of major projects for those responsible for sanctioning, financing or insuring such undertakings.

Project concept brief/proposal A short document that outlines the rationale, goals and scope of a project, prepared for the purposes of seeking early in-principle support for a project idea.

Project/s director Title used sometimes for the leader of a single large project, but often for a member of the organisation's executive or senior management team who has responsibility for strategy and innovation, including leading a group of projects.

Project initiation document (PID)   One of the most important artefacts in project management, because it provides a foundation for the project. It specifies why the project is important, what will be delivered, when it will be delivered and how.

Project life cycle   A framework of the phases that a project must move through in order to progress from 'a good idea' to completion.

Project management   The methods by which those responsible for a project make it happen and monitor and control the time, cost and quality of the project.

Project Management Office (PMO)   Is a group or department within a business, agency or enterprise that defines and maintains standards for project management within the organisation.

Project manager   The person responsible for managing the whole project, across the various departments and staff who may be needed.

Project portfolio   The collection of projects being conducted by the organisation, or by major divisions within it.

Project triangle   The three dimensions that define the project: quality (or specifications), time and resources.

Proof of Concept (POC)   A small exercise to test the design idea or assumption and to demonstrate functionality to verify a certain concept or theory that can be achieved in development.

RAG reporting   Project progress reports often use the traffic light rating system or RAG (Red, Amber, Green) status definition as a visual cue to project performance.

Risk matrix   A matrix that is used during risk assessment to define the level of risk by considering the category of probability or likelihood against the category of consequence severity.

Scope   The reach and boundaries of the project—'who, what, where, when and how'—within defined limits.

Scope creep   Unmanaged changes to scope—usually expansion.

Scrum   A system or software development method.

Sign-off   Formal approval.

Soft projects   Complex undertakings aimed at intangible results.

Sponsor   The executive who manages, administers, monitors, funds and is responsible for the overall project delivery.

Stage   A distinct part of a large project with its own outputs or deliverables; stages are often separated by decision points.

Stakeholders Individuals and organisations actively involved in the project, or whose interests may be affected as a result of the project, or who may exert influence over the project and its results.

Status report Advice to the steering committee, project sponsor and other stakeholders as to whether the project is on track to deliver the planned outcomes, and to highlight where their decision-making or direct help is needed.

Steering committee A formal advisory committee of high-level project-stakeholder representatives and/or experts, normally chaired by the project sponsor, that provides guidance on key issues, acts as the decision-making body for large changes to the project during its life, authorises acceptance of reports and deliverables, and acts as a sounding board for the project team.

Systematic literature review (see also Literature review) The review of literature focusing on a specific research question. The process includes identifying, appraising, selecting and synthesising all high-quality research evidence relevant to that question.

Tender An offer submitted by interested bidders (organisations that apply or 'bid' to win the contract) to the agency commissioning the project (sometimes called the 'purchaser').

Tracking Monitoring the progress of the project by determining how and when activities and milestones need to be reviewed.

Variance(s) A measurable change from a known standard or baseline—the difference between what is expected and what is actually accomplished.

Waterfall A system or software development method.

Work breakdown structure (WBS) A tool that the project team uses to plan the strategies, activities and tasks required to achieve the deliverables (and the goal) of the project. WBS enables detailed planning of the work, budget and timeline required for the project.

Work package All scheduled activities and tasks (with milestones) required to complete a deliverable in a WBS.

List of figures, tables and cases

Figures

Tables

Cases

About the authors

Dr Judith Dwyer AM is an adjunct Professor in the Flinders University College of Medicine and Public Health, and is a former CEO of Southern Health Care Network in Melbourne, and of Flinders Medical Centre in Adelaide. She was for several years a Research Program Leader for the Lowitja Institute, Australia's national Aboriginal health research institute, and taught in the Flinders University Masters of Health Administration. Her research interests include the governance of the Australian health system, and Aboriginal health services and policy. In 2014, she received the Sidney Sax Medal for her outstanding lifelong contribution to the Australian health system.

Dr Zhanming Liang is a Senior Lecturer in the School of Psychology and Public Health at La Trobe University in Melbourne, and is the President of SHAPE (Society for Health Administration Programs in Education). She worked in diverse roles—including medical practitioner, planning and evaluation consultant and senior manager—before joining academia. Her current research interests include management competency development, competence assessment for health service managers, and building capacity in health service management training, education and research in Asian and Pacific countries.

Ms Valerie Thiessen is a senior consultant at MKM Health, and holds qualifications in health information management, health services management and project management. Her experience includes roles in health information, business management, project management and consulting roles in both the private and public sectors in Australia. More recently, Valerie has been involved in and consulted on a variety of projects including EMR, clinical, radiology, learning management and patient information system implementations.

Acknowledgements

We owe a particular debt of gratitude to our colleagues Professor Pauline Stanton and Dr Angelita Martini, who were co-authors of previous editions and made vital contributions to the thinking on which this book is based.

We are also indebted to the colleagues and students with whom we discussed their project stories, good and bad, and the principles and practices that guide their work. We would like to thank Rachel Meisner and Lou Williamson for their help with ideas and resources, Monisha Vaid Sandhu for assistance with the literature review, and Yayuan Luo and Zixin Deng for editorial assistance. Finally, our thanks go to Dannielle Viera and Courtney Lick, our editors at Allen & Unwin.

Introduction

This third edition came about because the use of projects is growing and becoming more sophisticated in health and community services, and the need for project management approaches that are tailored to the sector continues to grow. Since the last edition, managers, policymakers and professionals have continued to respond to great waves of change with energy and creativity, finding new ways of providing care, of doing business and of sustaining their teams and organisations. Real sustained gains in effectiveness and productivity have been made. But at the same time, it remains difficult to bring new methods into practice, to learn from research and to change old habits and ways of thinking. The approach and methods of project management have a rich contribution to make as people, professions and agencies continue to find effective ways to innovate, change and grow.

The industry uses an increasing range of project management methods and tools drawn from other industries, and from technical, planning, clinical and research disciplines, with adaptations to suit sector and project needs. In writing this new edition, we had many discussions about this fast-moving field and our own experience as project managers, and we are confident that a book drawing on the richness of the industry—with its many stories, challenges, dilemmas and successes—has much to offer.

Writing a book is a project, too, and our good ideas had to go through the many stages of definition and redefinition, planning and implementation, always under pressure of time. We read the published literature, talked with people active in project leadership and project management, reviewed the many sources of contemporary information on the internet and, of course, reflected with our friends and loved ones. We also wrote a plan, divided up the work, committed to deadlines and struggled to meet them. The plan was revisited more than once, some tasks were swapped around, and the business of integrating all our contributions to make sure that the whole was more than the sum of its parts was an important challenge.

There are features of this edition that we think will work well for readers who need a guide as they struggle with their projects (or their project portfolios), as well as for those who are studying project management, or funding and commissioning projects. This book seeks to address a growing need in the health and community services sector for concise and critical guidance in the use of projects: when to use the project approach, how to design projects for success and how to choose among the many methods and tools. The need for guidance is growing, because more and more of what needs to be done in the sector is being conceived of, funded and managed as projects—while most of the literature on project management is designed for the engineering, IT or manufacturing industries. We aim to provide the information and the analytical framework that organisations, and current and aspiring managers and project managers, require in order to run successful projects, for the right outcomes, in a way that enhances the overarching purpose or strategy of their organisations.

How to use this book

The book can be read from start to finish for an experience of immersion in the world of projects and project management. Or parts can be used as a reference and guide by project managers at various stages of their work. Senior managers and those who decide which projects to approve and fund might use it to enhance their appreciation of what is needed for their good ideas to be implemented, and to improve their decision-making about which project proposals to support.

Chapter 1 explains the basics, and provides a model for thinking about project success and failure. Chapter 2 addresses the context of health and community services, and the factors that assist organisations to be successful in their project work. It suggests criteria that both senior managers and funders of projects could use to assist in their decision-making (that can also be used by those seeking to get their projects approved to improve their chances). Chapter 3 explains the project life cycle, gives an overview of the methods and tools of project management, and discusses career pathways for those with a talent for 'getting good ideas to work'. These three chapters establish the basis for the detailed guide to managing a project that makes up the following chapters.

Chapter 6 is new for this edition, and it explains the purpose and methods of evaluating project success, a critical but often neglected requirement for most projects, although our research for this book indicates that this situation may be changing. Chapters 4, 5, 7, 8 and 9 address the practice of project management, according to the phases of the project life cycle—initiation, planning, implementation and closure. The use of a broad range of methods, approaches and tools is explained, along with the challenge of making change happen through projects. These chapters are designed to meet the needs of both the practising project manager and those entering the field of project management. They are also important for those who manage groups of projects, plan project strategy for their organisations, or lead the planning and development effort.

Throughout the book, worked examples and project stories are used to illustrate the methods and tools. We have included lots of headings and subheadings in each chapter to help the reader locate particular topics of interest, as well as understand the logical development of the material. A summary at the end of each chapter recaps the major points, and case studies and useful checklists are highlighted within the text for easy reference. Additional resources are listed at the end of most chapters.

There is a lot of technical language in the world of projects, which we seek to explain and demystify throughout. Terms that might be unfamiliar are explained in the glossary at the beginning of this book, and shown in **bold** type the first time they appear in each chapter.

We are now at the satisfying moment of handover—the work has been done, celebrations have been held, and all the documentation is in order. For this project, the final evaluation will come later, and is in the hands of our readers.

1

Why project management?

This chapter explains what projects are and how projects are used by organisations, including those in health and community services. It also discusses why project management is important, and what project management can deliver. It covers the origins and development of project management as a method, and the reasons for its increasing popularity. We briefly discuss the results of a review of the literature that informs this edition of the book, and the chapter ends with a model for success in project management in health and community services.

What is a project?

> A temporary endeavour undertaken to create a unique product
> or service or result.
>
> *(PMI 2017, p. 4)*

A project is a unique set of interrelated **activities** designed to produce a set of **deliverables** and achieve a defined **goal** within clearly defined time, cost and quality constraints (Westland 2006). That is, a project is a one-off effort, requires resources and is often described as having a '3D' objective: to meet specifications, to finish on time and to be done within **budget** (see Figure 1.1). This is called the **project triangle** or 'iron triangle' (Atkinson 1999; Westerveld 2003).

The business of bringing together people and resources to achieve a one-off purpose (such as building a pyramid) has been one of the defining features of human society for as long as we can imagine. However, **project management** tools first emerged in engineering in the early 1900s, with the projects simply being managed by the architects, engineers and builders themselves. From the 1950s, project management tools and techniques were systematically applied to engineering and spread to other fields, such as construction and defence activity (Cleland & Gareis 2006). Since then, the rapid development of modern

Figure 1.1 The project 'iron triangle'

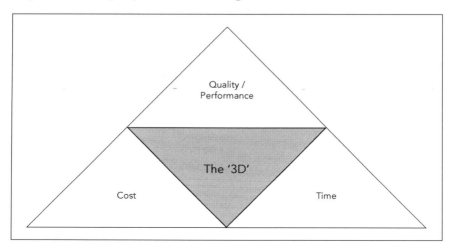

project management has seen it recognised as a distinct discipline, with two major worldwide professional organisations: the International Project Management Association (IPMA), established in 1967, and the Project Management Institute (PMI), in 1969. The PMI publishes a popular project management guidebook—*A Guide to the Project Management Body of Knowledge* (PMBOK® Guide)—and it specifies projects more formally as:

> Projects are undertaken to fulfil objectives by producing deliverables. An objective is defined as an outcome toward which work is to be directed, a strategic position to be attained, a purpose to be achieved, a result to be obtained, a product to be produced, or a service to be performed. A deliverable is defined as any unique and verifiable product, result, or capability to perform a service that is required to be produced to complete a process, phase, or project.
>
> *(PMI 2017, p. 4)*

The temporary nature of a project indicates a definite beginning and end. The end is reached when the project's objectives have been achieved or when the project is terminated because its objectives will not or cannot be met, or because the need for the project no longer exists. However, projects can have social, economic and environmental impacts that far outlast their end dates.

In the past twenty years, we have seen increasing attention given to projects in health and community services, with project management being recognised as one of the required competencies for health care managers (Sie & Liang 2015). As a result, most postgraduate courses in health care management, public health and health promotion incorporate project management competencies into the curriculum.

Although each project is unique, they all have some common characteristics. By definition, they are one-off efforts to achieve a goal, with a beginning and end as well as a budget/resources. They also have a common life cycle; have defined deliverables that are achieved and can be measured during or at the end of the project; and may enable changes that transform processes, performance and culture (Newton 2012; Roberts 2011; Turner 2007). Projects are also opportunities to create new knowledge and techniques to improve practice.

Projects have several characteristics that can make them challenging. First, each project is a *unique* and novel endeavour (Olsen 1971; Westland 2006), so, by definition, it hasn't been done before. This is one of the reasons why the original project design is often modified during project implementation, and why monitoring to identify and respond to early warning signs is often critical to project success. Second, depending on its size, the project may also require the involvement of many different occupational groups, different parts of the organisation, and different functions and resources, and these must be brought together to focus on the achievement of the **objectives** of the project. Team dynamics can also be critical when a wide range of roles, skills and expertise is required by the project.

Third, the targets set by a project are often *complex* and can require levels of technical performance not yet generally achieved in the field (Olsen 1971; Westland 2006). Complexity can arise from the different perspectives of various disciplines involved, the inexperience of the players, the number of interested parties, the geographic spread, the quantum of change, technical/solution complexity and so on. For example, hospital redevelopment projects are typically very complex undertakings involving constructing a new facility (often on an existing site), introducing new technology and procedures, and changing the size and structure of the staff, while also continuing to offer services. In a project such as this, important **stakeholders** may be opposed to one another, different departments with different agendas will be participating and political involvement will be high. All of these factors can have an impact on decision-making, the project **scope**, the communication challenge and the chances of success or failure.

Fourth, managing a project also means managing a *dynamic* situation, as the unexpected is always happening (Cleland & King 2008). When a new problem arises, it must be addressed immediately, because the project is limited by its timelines. Changes and modifications may add significant costs to the project budget. For example, it is expensive to change the specifications of a new Information and Communication Technology system once design work is underway. It can be expensive in a different way to change the goals or scope of an organisational restructuring project. Senior management can dictate a change of direction to respond to changes in the internal or external environments, but doing so is likely to damage commitment and goodwill among those affected, who often value certainty.

Projects can *vary in scope* from something as simple as implementing the use of a new type of catheter to a complex undertaking such as introducing a new model of care. Projects may impact and be visible to the whole organisation and wider community—glamorous and exciting—or they may be hidden away in a small team or department—committed people doing good work.

Managing projects can be similar to managing *high-risk* businesses (Chen 2011; Westland 2006). Projects are often used to trial new ideas, so there is a lot of uncertainty and some unknowns. For large projects, estimation of time and cost can be more an art than a science, based more on the experience of the project manager than sophisticated modelling. Projects can also be at risk from external factors such as stakeholder resistance, political intervention, changes of policy direction and funding cuts.

The project life cycle

Although projects are highly varied in almost every characteristic, they all move through a common basic life cycle—from initiation to closing, via planning/preparation and implementation phases. Figure 1.2 shows a model of the **project life cycle** in these four phases. Thinking about the phases in a project life cycle is useful both for seeing the whole picture and for planning and managing each phase. But it would be a mistake to think that having an idea, conceptualising the idea into a project, and

Figure 1.2 Project life cycle

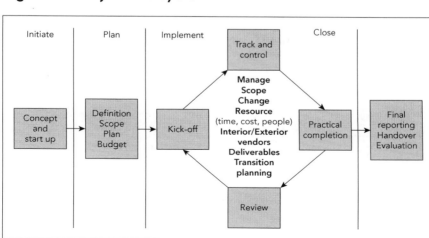

successfully completing the project is a linear process. Projects generally don't go exactly as planned, and **project managers** have a critical role in monitoring progress, identifying problems or variations, modifying the plan and taking action accordingly.

Although it is useful to plan and manage the project in phases, the phases are not really separate—rather, they tend to overlap and often lack clear boundaries. Even when the team is using a project management method with formal approval steps, there may not be an obvious point where they can say 'the initiation phase is complete, we are now starting the planning phase'. Projects can also go backwards—for example, problems in the project planning or implementation can force a rethink of the original concept and/or a redesign of the project.

There are also activities that continue throughout the project, such as stakeholder management, change management, evaluation activities, risk management and monitoring of progress. The project life cycle is addressed in more detail in Chapter 3.

Projects in health and community services

The use of project management methods is well established in the health and community services industry. Staff in local government, and in community health centres, began defining much of their community development and health promotion work as projects in the 1970s and 1980s, and developed in-house templates and protocols to plan and manage their work. These methods have proven effective, and managing by projects is now standard practice in these fields.

Government and hospitals have been using project management methods for capital and information and communication technology (ICT) projects for many years, but widespread application of these methods to their core business began largely in the 1990s. In recent years, projects have been used to introduce changes such as new care processes and service improvement, as well as for much larger changes such as organisation restructuring and implementation of information systems and reforms in the health sector. The introduction of continuous quality improvement methods and process re-engineering also provided important sources of project thinking and project skill development.

Our review of the project management literature confirmed a substantial increase in published research on project management in health and community services in the past ten years. Project management tools and methods are reported to have been widely used, particularly to improve quality and safety and to reduce costs, with more case studies being published in recent years.

Government health and human service departments, on the other hand, initially tended to focus on in-house project development and approval processes, and workflow management methods. More recently, there has also been an increase in the use of project management tools and software to guide project work. Many government departments are skilled users of contracted projects, and there has often been a transfer of project skills from the consultants to departmental staff. The **procurement**, **commissioning** and funding of projects in health and community services, in order to test new ideas and develop new services, has been a common method of encouraging innovation, quality improvement and the move into new models of care or modes of service delivery.

In health and community services, project management methods are used for six major purposes:

1. The development of new services, **programs** or technologies.
2. To improve existing services, care processes, work practices or service delivery models.
3. The implementation of new organisational structures or systems.
4. The conduct of procurement processes, for example new equipment, ICT systems, or to engage management consultants (de Araújo et al. 2017; Yeow & Edler 2012).
5. The construction, acquisition and/or commissioning of new equipment and facilities.
6. To conduct research projects, such as evidence reviews, needs studies and service planning (Swiatek et al. 2016).

The first four of these purposes are fundamentally about the management of change and basic organisational strategy. For success in this kind of project, change management principles should apply, and it is critical for project managers to understand the impact of the project on themselves and other staff (Levasseur 2010). The experience of Australian hospitals in projects to improve the flow of patients through emergency departments is a good example. These projects set out to achieve change to longstanding work practices and relationships. While some of the difficulties are technical (for example, lack of good automated information systems for managing patient flow), the more significant problems arise from the need to change the roles of clinical staff, and the relationships among different medical specialties (Proudlove et al. 2003). These and other considerations also have an impact on the question of how to sustain changes in operations after the project stage is complete (Willis et al. 2016).

Research for this book

To guide the development of this edition, we conducted a methodical literature review focusing on the development of project management and relevant concepts in health and community services over the past ten years. The results of the literature review have been used throughout the book. In total, 155 journal articles focused on the following aspects of projects and project management were found and analysed:

1. project design and approaches
2. difficulties in design and implementation
3. evaluation of projects
4. success factors
5. project examples or case studies
6. evidence reviews.

The literature suggests that there are several areas of health and community services work to which project management principles and techniques are increasingly applied, including research, procurement and the development of new products and services. There was significant work on the application of project management principles and skills to organisational or service change, along with new literature discussing project management in developing countries, and a number of systematic literature reviews focusing on ICT and Electronic Health Record (EHR) implementation projects. The experience of 'megaprojects' has also been documented, highlighting the importance of three major elements: clear strategic vision, total alignment, and adapting to complexity.

Evaluation of project outcomes and benefits continues, with growth in evaluation studies focused on the performance and success of project management itself: measuring elements such as team performance and sustainability strategies. This increasing focus on project evaluation affirmed the need for a new chapter on this topic (Chapter 6).

Project management challenges

General management skills and methods are useful in managing projects, but by themselves are not enough—projects require some different approaches, methods and tools from those used for managing routine operations. Project management is defined as the application of skills and the use of methods, tools and techniques designed to conduct project activities and to enable organisations to plan, manage and achieve one-off tasks or goals (Meredith & Mantel 2012). Project managers must solve the problems of defining what is needed, planning how to deliver it at the defined standard of quality, managing the required resources in a timely and efficient manner, ensuring successful delivery and bedding down the outcomes. To put it another way, project management is a series of processes to monitor and control the time, cost and quality of projects (Westland 2006).

The need for project management skills is most clearly seen in large and complex projects. For example, the implementation of the case-mix funding model in Australian public hospitals as part of national health reform brought many changes, not only to clinical services and support units but also to administrative systems, financial analysis and reporting and information systems. The use of project management approaches allowed better planning and use of resources and better implementation, as staff worked across departmental boundaries to prepare and cope with the changes. Skilled project management provides a focal point for the work of integrating new functional efforts through a (temporary) organisational structure that supports rather than stifles change (Kerzner 2009).

This is one of many examples of major changes in models of care and policy frameworks since the 1990s. Others include integrated mental health services, family-centred care, multipurpose health centres, shared care programs, transitional care and case management. Project management has been an effective means to design and implement new processes, allocate resources, streamline operations and develop new skills. It also allows new technologies and initiatives to be integrated into the organisations more effectively and efficiently.

Project management offers a method for driving development processes and successfully implementing change. Successful project management enables organisations to remain relevant and competitive, and to continuously improve products, services and processes. Project management is also important in responding to a crisis—for example, in the development and deployment of disaster plans. This is necessarily a multidisciplinary and interagency process that can significantly impact on the wellbeing of the entire community or a whole population. However, the increasing use of projects means that project management knowledge, skills and abilities are needed by virtually all health managers, not only those who specialise in project management.

The translation of management tools and techniques from industry generally to the health sector is often difficult, requiring major alterations to suit the sector. Sometimes the promised benefits are not realised. Project management is just such an adopted method, and much of the literature does not adequately address the problems that arise in an industry so dominated by skilled professional labour, and so intimately linked to the processes and complexities of government and public policy. This raises two questions: What problems are encountered in the sector? And are the methods of project management robust enough for application in the sector?

Like any method, project management can be well or badly suited to its chosen use, and can be well or badly used. Properly used, it has the potential to enhance the organisation's ability to innovate and grow, bring discipline to the processes of change, and enable organisations to focus more strongly on their purpose and the outcomes they need to achieve. In our attempt to provide insights into effective use of projects, we believe it is important to proceed from an understanding of the typical problems encountered in project management in health and community services. There are several challenges that health and community service organisations in particular need to meet in order to maximise the gains from the projects they conduct, described in Table 1.1.

Is it the sector or is it the method?

In Table 1.1, we outline five challenges that the sector needs to address to get the maximum value from its use of the project approach. An alternative explanation needs to be considered. Are these issues indicators of weaknesses in the method rather than of problems in the sector?

In a sense, projects are simply segments of the ongoing, complicated and sometimes messy business of the organisations in which they sit, with an artificial line drawn around them and some special rules and resources applied. The theoretical model of the project gives it a clear,

Table 1.1 Project management challenges in the health and community services

Challenges	Details
The agenda: strategy or opportunism	Ideally, projects contribute to the achievement of organisational strategic directions. However, projects in health and community services are often the result of responses to changes in government policy and initiatives, and to funding opportunities. Some organisations face challenges in getting real benefits out of all the projects they commit to.
Contested ground: 'You can't change that!'	Projects are widely used to achieve change. However, change is difficult in the complex and politicised environment of health and community services, with multiple empowered stakeholders and other conditions that enable effective resistance. Projects flounder and sometimes fail because they are trying to achieve things that are at odds with the team or organisational culture, or which require unwelcome change in work practices, power relationships or ways of working together; or simply because they are too big to 'chew'.
Hope is not a method	People working in health and community services are accustomed to living with complex goals that outstrip the ability of their organisations to deliver, and they sometimes fail to meet the expectations of the community. Sometimes, projects are designed to convince policymakers and other key players to pursue a social policy goal by demonstrating how it can work in practice. This strategy can succeed, but issues like 'on time and on budget' are hardly relevant when 'specifications' are a moving target, or have many shapes in the eyes of several different stakeholders.
Knowing how: tools, techniques and methods	Although the use of project management methods and tools is important to project success, many were designed and tested in general industry. They often give inadequate attention to the complexities of multiple stakeholders, multiple agendas and the politics of change that so often underlie project failure in the health and community services sector. Furthermore, the tools themselves may be too rigid to use when most projects in the sector require a high level of flexibility.
Sustainability: did we get there?	Often, the goal of testing new ideas through successful completion of projects is to implement ongoing programs or services. The project benefits can prove difficult to sustain if little thought has been given to how results might be integrated, or what level of resources and support will be needed to sustain them. Another challenge is how to develop and sustain the organisation's project capacity— keeping their good project managers, and embedding the skills of project management as part of their organisational knowledge.

uncontested goal, a set of technical requirements that must be fulfilled to meet the goal, and a set of methods and tools for doing so. In theory, the results are then handed back to grateful operating units, which use them to achieve transformational change (Shao et al. 2012) and move forward to a brighter, more effective and more competitive future.

But in reality, no project exists in isolation (Engwell 2003), and organisations work with complex goals and contested structures, policies and methods. Internal projects must deal with stakeholders who are in effect both the subjects and the objects of change—that is, the change makers and the changed. Thus, the project team may need to change the roles, mindsets or privileges of the very people who must endorse the project's goals and outcomes. Effective engagement and maintaining stakeholder interest and commitment is always a challenge (Eskerod & Huemann 2013). In addition, projects may bring their own bureaucracy and, paradoxically, are resistant to change in the project itself while advocating the use of projects to pursue organisational change. Finally, if the methods of project management are not built on an adequate research and theory base, their claims to universal application cannot be justified.

This book is our answer to the question that started this section: is the method sufficiently robust to serve the needs of the health and community services sector? And the answer is 'yes, for the right purposes and with modifications'. The rest of this book outlines how and why.

Project success

The definition of a project suggests that the criteria of project success are meeting cost, schedule, and performance targets (Belassi & Tukel 1996), and early studies adopted these criteria, often focusing on the reasons for project failure. More recent definitions of project success are broader, encompassing success of the management of the project, success of the project output, and the realisation of defined benefits (Williams 2015). In reality, the picture is more complex—many projects go over time and budget but are still judged to be successful by participants for a variety of other reasons.

Table 1.2 gives examples of how project success may be defined from three important perspectives: those of project **sponsors** (this may include senior management of the organisation), project managers and key stakeholders (including consumers).

Table 1.2 Defining project success from different perspectives

Project sponsor	• Have the expected benefits been achieved? • Have the potential long-term gains been maximised? • Have we funded the right people to do the job, and have we got the best return for the financial investment? • Has the project contributed to the achievement of organisational objectives? • Are the project users/customers satisfied with what they received? • Has the leadership of the organisation enabled project success?
Project manager	• Has the project been completed on schedule and within budget? • Have all activities been completed and all 'outputs' delivered as planned? • Have changes been managed according to sponsors' expectations along the way? • Have any detrimental effects, risks or issues been minimised? • Has the project team stayed motivated and focused? • Have the key stakeholders been well managed and engaged? • Have all the necessary project records been kept for reporting and future use?
Stakeholders	• Have we received the best services/products possible? • Have the benefits been maximised? • Are the benefits sustainable for the long term? • Have my needs and expectations been heard/met? • Is this the best way to meet my needs and address my concerns? • Are the overall outcomes of the project satisfactory?

The project/organisational context also needs to be considered, including economic, social and environmental aspects (Martens & Carvalho 2016). Researchers have found that projects often have unexpected side effects, 70 per cent of which could be attributed to lack of awareness of the environment (White & Fortune 2002). These authors suggest that in many of the methods used, 'insufficient account was taken of project boundaries and environments' (White & Fortune 2002, p. 5). Some of the side effects were beneficial to the organisation—for example, an increase in business, sales or opportunities, or gaining new knowledge and understanding. However, the undesirable effects were wide-ranging and included organisational conflicts and problems with staff, clients, contractors and/or suppliers, as well as technical limitations. Some organisations in this study reported that the project resulted in greater organisational complexity (and this is confirmed by Meredith & Mantel 2012). An example in health and community services is that health promotion projects may lead to increases in demand for screening, diagnosis and care—a good outcome from a health perspective, but perhaps a negative side effect for local service providers.

Sometimes, a project may prove that the models or approaches proposed will not work or will not produce the intended benefits. It is also important for staff involved in projects to understand that, in reality, even successful projects may not lead to further actions or result in new services or program development. Therefore, no set rules can be used to quantify project success, and it cannot be judged without reference to the views of those who are involved and affected.

Model for success

Many authors have sought to determine the **critical success factors** (CSF) for achieving desired project outcomes, on the basis of studies of project success since the 1960s. The most significant early study on critical success factors (Pinto & Slevin 1988) identified ten factors that determine success regardless of project type, and these were further tested and mainly reinforced by a number of subsequent studies (Andersen et al. 2006; Fortune & White 2006; Hassan et al. 2017; Mishra et al. 2011; Osei-Kyei & Chan 2017; Yalegama et al. 2016). They are:

- project mission (clear goals and direction)
- top management support
- project planning
- client consultation (engagement of stakeholders)
- people management
- technical tasks (having the needed technology and expertise)
- client acceptance (sign-off)
- monitoring and feedback
- communication
- trouble shooting.

Of all the factors, project quality (including clear vision and goals), strong leadership and effective communications have been consistently highlighted (for example, Assudani & Kloppenborg 2010; Chen 2011; Rosacker et al. 2010;). But long lists of critical success factors are not always helpful. We have re-analysed the evidence, with a particular focus on the more recent studies, and summarised the wealth of success factors in five categories as shown in Table 1.3.

The final category, the project environment, highlights the fact that some of the success of projects is due to factors in the organisation or the broader context. Some organisations are more able to get good results from all their projects, and some environmental influences affect

Table 1.3 Project critical success factors

1.	Project design • Project goals and objectives are clear, realistic and based on understanding of local context. • Stakeholder engagement and good communication are designed in. • Needed training for the project team and relevant staff is part of the project design.
2.	Leadership and management competence • Project sponsor/leader and manager understand organisation politics and the complex project environment. • Project manager shows strong leadership of the team, and gives timely support and feedback. • Project processes and methods are competently managed. • Good communication with all stakeholders (including project team). • Risk identification and management strategies are applied.
3.	Project team performance • Team members are committed to success. • Team members have the relevant knowledge and experience. • The team is able to anticipate and respond to project challenges. • The team respects the project parameters and members accept accountability for accomplishing tasks.
4.	Resources • Training relevant to specific project requirements is provided. • Technical resources are provided and ICT support is available as needed. • Budget is adequate and timelines are realistic.
5.	Project environment • Stakeholders are committed to project success. • The organisation pursues continuous improvement. • Other parts of the organisation support the project. • The organisation's policies and procedures are useful to guide project processes, and don't create barriers.

all organisations. The industry and organisational factors that enable or constrain project success are discussed in Chapter 2.

Summary

- Projects are a way of achieving a one-off goal. They are unique, complex and vary in scope; and need to achieve defined goals within clearly defined time, cost and quality constraints.
- There is a wealth of methods and tools available to support this work.
- Managing a project is not a simple linear process, but rather has a life cycle of four phases: initiation, planning, implementation and closure.
- The invention of the role of the project manager was a significant breakthrough, enabling organisations to lead and coordinate all the people and resources required for the project to succeed.
- Projects are being used more and more frequently in a world of constant change and increasing complexity, but health and community service organisations encounter some particular challenges in achieving the anticipated value from their project work and in managing their project portfolios.
- The available critiques of project management have relevance to the sector, and argue for modification of the mainstream methods to suit the needs of the sector (hence this book).
- Project success involves more than achieving the project's intended outcomes within the time and cost allowed—it is also influenced by the interests of internal and external stakeholders and by unintended effects.
- The determinants of project success have been extensively studied since the 1960s. On the basis of this evidence, we have developed a framework for understanding project success factors that is intended to be useful to senior managers, project sponsors, managers and teams in setting up their projects for success, and in understanding what goes wrong.

Readings and resources

Association for Project Management: www.apm.org.uk/
Australian College of Project Management: www.projectmanagement.edu.au/
Longest, B.B., 2004, *Managing Health Programs and Projects*, San Francisco, CA: Jossey-Bass

Martin, V., 2002, *Managing Projects in Health and Social Care*, New York, NY: Routledge

Project Management Association of Canada: www.pmac–ampc.ca/

Project Management Institute (PMI), 2017, *A Guide to the Project Management Body of Knowledge*, 8th edn, Newtown Square, PA: PMI Inc

Project Management Institute: www.pmi.org

Roberts, P., 2011, *Effective Project Management: Identify and manage risk, plan and budget, keep projects under control,* London: Kogan Page

The Australian Institute of Project Management: www.aipm.com.au

2

The industry, the organisation and project success

In this chapter, we explain aspects of the industry environment that influence project work and the organisational factors that help to determine the chances of project success. We then propose key criteria for choosing and shaping projects that can be adapted and used by leaders and managers to help them make decisions about what projects to do and how to shape them for their own setting (these criteria will also be useful for middle managers seeking to improve their success in getting their projects approved).

The industry: complex, regulated—and still dynamic

Projects are different in different settings, and every industry has characteristics that change the way projects are done. The challenges outlined in Chapter 1 are not unique to health and community services, but they do have particular causes and effects in the sector. For readers without direct experience of working in the sector, the following information explains some important background.

Structural features of the health and community services environment

Government regulation and funding: The industry, in both public and private sectors, is highly regulated—and at least partly funded—by government, and so is subject to the vagaries of government policy change and ways of doing business. While this situation creates opportunities for growth, it restricts strategic choices, particularly for organisations in the public sector, to set their own directions. It also requires leaders to find compromises between the demands of government and the needs or priorities of their own organisation. Projects can be part of the problem here (as well as being opportunities), if project portfolios are shaped largely by government agendas, regardless of their internal priority.

Dynamic change in policy and practice: The industry is dynamic and much of it is constantly engaged in change and development. This means that there is always room to find better ways of working, and it can enable staff to muster great energy and commitment. However, it can also lead to important staff groups pulling in different and sometimes contradictory directions. Leaders are subjected to increasing demands for service development and the allocation of new resources, while budgets are always constrained. Staff get 'change fatigue', and project effort can be spread too thin.

People-rich environment: This is a people-rich industry, with many tertiary-educated staff who are used to exercising professional independence and are organised into powerful professional and trade union groups. Leaders are accustomed to standing on contested ground, with some sections of the workforce agitating for change and others (those with something to lose) digging in or refusing to engage. This means that stakeholder engagement is both critical and challenging.

High social values: The critical social role of the industry means that politicians, the media and the community have strong views about services and standards, and this can result in both pressure for change, and resistance to it from inside and outside the organisation. This impacts on the initiatives organisations seek to implement through projects, and on the ways that projects are managed.

In health and community services, there are four main ways that these characteristics of the industry impact directly on the way projects are done (and how well they work). They are the influence of governments on the project agenda; the extent to which projects are used as a way to implement change; the funding and resourcing of projects; and the challenges of stakeholder management.

The role of government

Governments and other funders have a major impact on the project portfolios of health and community services. While this is true in both the private and public sectors, it is more acute for government-funded agencies. In the later years of the 20th century, governments increasingly took up an active role as 'purchasers' of particular services (rather than passive subsidisers of provider organisations).

Initially, this shift brought increased use of project funding as a strategy for encouraging change in practice and models of care, and for enhancing government's ability to monitor and control agencies. Direct government funding programs for improvement and innovation projects enabled cash-strapped agencies to invest in updating their services, to bring in new approaches more suited to current needs and technologies, and to enhance their capacity to analyse service data.

However, governments have largely changed their approach in recent years, and are more likely to rely on financial incentives (or penalties) and/or tighter specification of what is to be done. Public hospitals and health services in particular experience increasing use of regulation and performance standards to drive improvement efforts. Leaders (including those in government health departments) face tighter constraints in their choice of projects, and increasing requirements to respond to policy and funding changes—for example, tobacco policy, activity- and performance-based funding, national emergency access targets, electronic health record implementation, greater emphasis on coordination of care across agencies, and other aspects of continuing national health reform. There is also an increased presence of national government-owned organisations that are effectively project-based (that is, structured primarily to deliver a set of projects commissioned by government), such as the Australian Digital Health Agency, which is charged with 'improving health outcomes for Australians through the delivery of digital healthcare systems and the national digital health strategy for Australia' (Australian Digital Health Agency 2018).

The Agency's projects cover a broad spectrum of activity including eHealth standards, telehealth, health identifiers, information exchange, health terminologies and software development. They touch every part of the health sector: primary care, community care, health services, health insurers, diagnostic providers, aged care and technology providers. However, given the nature of the work, development needs to be driven centrally, and so the projects tend to be shared nationally with state and territory health authorities and/or be contracted out to major suppliers. The health services are largely recipients rather than drivers of this project agenda, although hospital and health services staff are involved as stakeholders.

Regardless of the methods governments use, government policy and funding is and will remain a strong influence on project agendas. This is not in itself a problem—government has a responsibility to determine both policy and the use of taxpayer funds. But health and community service providers have a different set of responsibilities, and different imperatives. They must attend to the capacity of the organisation, to the coordinated delivery of the right services to meet client/patient needs, and to the shaping of a coherent strategy to achieve the agency's purpose, all within usually tight budget constraints. For public health and community services, their purpose and roles may well have been determined by the funder, but the providers' imperative to make it work remains. In the private sector, many services are funded by government, and government regulation of incentives and standards is an important influence, and sometimes a constraint, on operations and service delivery.

There is thus a real risk that regulation and national reform agendas will become too strong a driver of the agency's attention, energy and resources, usurping the role that strategic directions and business strategies should play.

Using projects to implement change

When an engineering firm builds a bridge, its outcome can be measured on completion in terms of quality (is it sound and fit for purpose?), cost and timeliness. When a health service designs a new way of delivering an aspect of health care, its effectiveness can usually not be measured until well after the project is complete. Will the new model be fully implemented? Will it work better (or as well as) the old way for patients' health outcomes? Will the intended cost savings (or reallocation of resources) be achieved at the time anticipated? Will there be perverse effects on the overall budget of the health service (such as costs being incurred in the health service, and savings being realised in other organisations)? Will the model be sustainable?

When projects are used as methods for designing and implementing change, there is usually a high level of uncertainty associated with their initial specification, the processes used and the embedding of the outcome. Change projects usually extend out from the boundaries of the project as defined, and such projects 'cannot be judged with concepts stemming from the methods of construction project management' (Dobers & Söderholm 2009, p. 481).

Resourcing projects

Competition for project resources within organisations is widespread and important. In many organisations, the most common reasons for project proposals failing to get approval are financial, and this means both cost per se and the strength of the **business case**—that is, the potential for the project results to generate a positive financial impact that justifies the costs and effort.

For private sector organisations, the direct need to generate a financial return on investment imposes discipline on decisions to authorise projects, while also enabling leaders to support promising projects. In the public sector, cost-saving and cost-neutrality (that is, an alternative way of doing things should cost no more than is currently being spent) are important considerations in decision-making. However, there is less capacity to balance costs with enhanced revenue (because revenue is at least partly set by government), which means that it can be very hard to find resources even for important and valuable projects. This is an enduring feature of the industry, and one that underlies several reasons for project failure, including inadequate staffing and budgets, and unrealistic timing.

Managing stakeholders

One of the most difficult challenges in project management in the sector is managing the key stakeholders: the people and groups (within and outside the organisation) who are affected by the project, who can influence its design and conduct, and who usually have different and competing agendas. The risk is that the person with the loudest voice or strongest personality can take a project in an undesirable direction based on conviction or self-interest.

For many projects, internal groups—staff, volunteers, clinical and other professional groups, and departments or units—are the main stakeholders. But there are also external stakeholders who might become involved in a project, perhaps through being part of a steering or advisory committee, being a project funder or a supplier (e.g. of information systems or equipment). Different professional and trade union organisations (and their internal representatives and members) may have their own sectoral interests that are beyond the scope of the project. They can stymie change and derail projects, sometimes deliberately, but sometimes because adherence to their own agendas does not allow them to see any alternatives.

Governments can also be key stakeholders. Government agencies can change their minds and alter their policy directions well into the project life cycle, due to a change in government or a change of key personnel, or because more important priorities come along. Governments are also susceptible to public opinion and political lobbying, and a project that has potential for unpopularity is vulnerable if strong community or political opposition is mobilised against it.

Consumers are another important stakeholder group that can be difficult for professional staff to engage and involve. Staff may question the capacity of consumers to contribute, or feel challenged by a shift in relative roles (from being 'in charge' to engaging with consumers as equals in considering problems and solutions). Consumers with a chronic condition might be too ill to participate for very long in a project, other consumers might be transitory and move on to other interests. Consumers can become disillusioned by their experiences in committees or reference groups—perhaps because their expectations are so high that they are never likely to be realised, or because they feel disempowered by the approaches of the professionals involved in the project management process. On the other hand, membership of committees may not be the best way to involve consumers or gather information about their priorities and needs, and a lot has been learned about both goals and effective approaches to involving consumers (see, for example, Consumers Health Forum of Australia 2017; Health Issues Centre 2018).

Sometimes the influence of powerful groups of people pulling in different directions leads to 'stakeholder paralysis', where nothing gets done and people become angry and frustrated. Case 2.1 outlines an alternative method for engaging stakeholders in the decision-making process. Maintaining stakeholder engagement throughout the life of the project is also sometimes a challenge. Managing stakeholders is addressed in depth in Chapters 5 and 8.

Case 2.1 Getting beyond stakeholder paralysis

A major metropolitan hospital was missing an opportunity to bill for work performed in its imaging service due to the established interpretation of a Medicare Billing guideline.

The hospital's long-held interpretation of the Medicare rules was that a test performed on the same day as a public outpatient appointment was not billable through Medicare, while a test performed on a separate day from an appointment was billable, as it was not considered to be within the bounds of the public appointment. This rule was applied regardless of the date of referral, so an X-ray taken prior to an appointment was also deemed not billable. Radiologists who worked at other hospitals had realised that those hospitals were billing for tests performed both before and after the appointment, and on the radiologists' request, the Business Manager estimated the revenue foregone at $1 million dollars each year.

This seemed like a simple change to implement—more revenue for the same work, no change to patient care, and a precedent that had been set by other hospitals. The Business Manager initiated a project to make the change, but encountered some major barriers from key stakeholders including some of the medical staff, the billing department and even members of the executive.

The barriers included unwillingness to challenge the established way, partly because the change was considered risky for the doctors (in whose names the bills would be charged to Medicare). There was also concern about the administrative burden of the additional billing. The situation was complicated by a poor working relationship between the radiologists and the executive, and a lack of engagement by the executive.

In order to overcome these barriers, the Business Manager brought together a small project group tasked with planning for and implementing the change. They undertook to complete:

- a peer review of practices in other organisations
- meetings with the doctors responsible for the billing and action to resolve their concerns about personal responsibility for the Medicare billing, in the form of a 'letter of comfort' from the CEO
- engagement and negotiation with the billing department, including negotiating additional resources for the extra work
- review of billing guidelines and legislation to provide comfort to the legal department
- engagement with the CEO.

Progress was slow, and there was a lot of resistance. The tipping point came when the Business Manager arranged for herself, the legal department and the CEO to meet, and pointed out that the CEO had previously sponsored the changed interpretation at a previous hospital, and if they couldn't get agreement at the meeting then the project should be cancelled. After much discussion, stakeholders at the meeting agreed to a revised interpretation of the rules that would result in an additional $750,000 per annum in revenue.

In reflecting on the turning point, the Business Manager realised that she had been up against empowered stakeholders in an organisation with a long history of seeing itself as a charity, and that being compliant was not going to work for her. She said about her assertiveness in the meeting that 'it was more chutzpah than proper process, but that's sometimes how things get done, right?' She said the CEO seemed quite amused, and 'it didn't hurt our relationship at all'.

Project capability in organisations

While important environmental and industry factors do have a strong impact on projects, organisational capability is critical (Better Care Victoria 2017; Roberts 2011). The health and community services field is large and diverse, but there are common factors at the level of the organisation that influence project success: strategic direction setting, leadership, culture (and climate) and approaches to the management of people. Leaders need to recognise these underlying influences and anticipate and manage their potential positive or negative impact on projects. The influence and support of government has promoted project maturity in many health organisations, and the practices and techniques of project management are recognised as being essential skills that benefit organisations (Andersen & Jessen 2003). This maturity is evident across a number of dimensions, including project management (and team) skills, the number and complexity of projects undertaken and the widespread use of project methodologies. The recognition of project management and maturity models has been evidenced over the last years by the large investments made by health organisations to develop competencies and skills (Gomes et al. 2016).

Strategic direction setting

Although projects 'stand-alone' with their specific goals and objectives, they also need to align with the organisation's strategic goals and be an integrated part of the organisation (Chen 2011).

Since the first edition of this book, we have noticed a stronger sense of control of project agendas, and a greater focus on proper resourcing and project governance. But managers still face the temptation to take on too many projects and the risk of not giving sufficient priority to critical issues.

There is now a stronger reliance on the discipline imposed by formal processes of development and approval, and also a greater emphasis on linking projects to the operational plan or business plan. Increasingly, strategy for some health and community service organisations is project-based—that is, their strategic changes are enacted largely as a portfolio of projects (for example, in preparing a home-based care organisation for the impact of new Australian government aged care funding and eligibility rules).

Whether the organisation's strategic directions and business plans support or hinder project success depends on two elements: how well projects align with the strategic directions and plans, and how strongly held those directions are. Firstly, the success of a project will depend partly on how it aligns with the organisation's strategies for achieving its basic purpose or mission. Secondly, the relative strength of the strategic direction (how strongly and broadly it is supported throughout the organisation) will impact on the ability of the organisation to muster coordinated support for a key project.

The reverse is also true: if the strategic directions are only weakly held, poorly aligned projects are less likely to be weeded out. That is, it is difficult to use the organisation's strategic directions as a test for the priority of particular funding opportunities if they are not strongly understood and valued by the majority of influential people and groups in the organisation. This can be a major source of difficulties with managing the project portfolio, and not only in human services. A classic study in the US pharmaceutical industry, for example, found that leaders in many of the firms surveyed singled out the organisation's inability to prioritise effectively as a key weakness, caused by 'countervailing organizational special interests' that were able to resist the portfolio-level decisions of senior management (Case 1998, p. 593).

While most health and community service organisations have a strategic directions document, in some cases there is not enough commitment or shared understanding throughout the organisation to allow it to drive decision-making from top leadership level down.

To look at this another way, the problem is not that there are no strategic directions, but rather that there are several competing and perhaps contradictory ones.

Internal politics is an ongoing reality—the interests of individuals, units and teams within the organisation will not always align with the organisation's broader interests or strategies, and the result is a leadership problem. Neither leaders nor projects can change this reality—part of what is sometimes called the 'shadow side' of organisations (Egan 1994)—but there are strategies for managing it. Strategic plans can be designed to recognise and better align the interests of important internal stakeholders with those of the organisation as a whole. Leaders can act to channel 'political' activity out of the corridors and into structured priority-setting processes. We return to this difficult question in Chapter 8.

Leadership at every level

Among all the important organisational elements, support from senior management (or management **buy-in**) and effective leadership are viewed as critical project success factors (for example, Shokri-Ghasabeh & Kavousi-Chabok 2009; Tabassi et al. 2017). Leadership is needed to ensure staff 'own' the project and understand how it fits into the overall direction of the organisation, as well as to marshall needed resources and support. And it is a project management truism that if you haven't got high-level endorsement and championing, it is very hard to make even a great idea work (Lundy & Morin 2013).

There is a paradoxical requirement for leaders—they need to both generate commitment and simultaneously impose discipline on project activity, a task that is challenging for all of the reasons outlined earlier in this chapter. This task applies at every level of the organisation, from the board of directors to project team members.

Culture and climate

It has become fashionable to describe organisational cultures according to their relevance for particular goals. Thus, management writers and consultants advocate for a 'quality culture', 'innovation culture', 'learning culture' or 'high performance culture', and project management writers are part of this trend (for example, Zuo et al. 2014).

Organisation culture is a much-discussed but ill-defined concept, which makes intuitive sense to most people who have worked in organisations but is hard to study and perhaps even harder to manipulate. By culture, we mean the unwritten values and rules that are understood and endorsed by the staff (or important subgroups) and therefore govern 'how things are done around here'.

Organisations with a culture that supports project success have three key characteristics: they have an ability to handle change; they have the ability to incorporate new knowledge—that is, to learn; and there is a broad awareness among staff of the project method and how it can be used. These characteristics, particularly the first two, are generally also seen as part of those other desired cultures (high performance, quality, and so on), and there is a vast literature on these questions (for example, Leggat & Dwyer 2005; Shore 2008; Yazici 2009). O'Kelly and Maxwell (2001) argue enthusiastically for the adoption of a project management culture in health care, particularly in relation to the implementation of clinical governance in the United Kingdom. For these authors, a project management culture implies an ability to initiate change and get things done in a manageable way through the use of project teams. Organisational leaders cannot change culture at will, but they can understand and encourage those aspects of the culture that support innovation, willingness to learn and the development of shared project capability.

Idealism is an issue for the management of individual projects in health and community services, as well as for the management of project portfolios—and not only in the public sector. Commitment to the 'public good' ethos is seen in committed effort to provide good services regardless of the barriers; in acceptance of ambiguity and complexity; and also in the difficulty experienced by many health and community service organisations in choosing priorities among competing needs or options. When judgements must be made about which worthy project to sacrifice and which to approve, the process of decision-making can be prolonged, emotional, politicised and less strategic than leaders would like to admit.

Perhaps the business culture that produced modern project management is more pragmatic, with more concrete goals and more direct methods of pursuing them, than is the health and community services culture. Ideals like 'quality, access, equity' are more complex and abstract than business slogans like 'faster, better, cheaper'.

The concept of team or organisational climate is perhaps more directly amenable to leadership attention. If culture is defined as 'how we do things around here', climate is 'how it feels to work here'. Typically, in a positive team climate, staff can answer yes to questions like: Are staff free to innovate? Can staff get on with their work without asking for permissions and guidance from the manager? Are goals high but attainable? Do staff know what is expected? Is good work recognised in a tangible way? Is there a sense of belonging to a winning team with shared goals? While it can be hard to put your finger on why some teams work well, our experience indicates that staff know when they are in a good team climate, and that much more can be achieved under these conditions.

Climate can be changed profoundly by good leadership. There is good evidence (for example, Edmondson 1999) that a team climate in which the leader enables staff to feel safe in questioning accepted ways of doing things creates the conditions for success in innovation. This is an important insight for leaders who seek to enhance the chances of project success.

While team commitment is positive, the related idealism that is part of health and community services culture can be a source of resistance to change. The 'missionary organisation' (Mintzberg 1991) is one that pursues values–based goals (such as relieving suffering or reducing inequality) and attracts staff who are personally driven by those goals. Their commitment, however, may lead them to resist what they perceive as incorrect interpretations of the mission. When this tendency is linked to self-interest (for example, a proposed change to a model of service that will require inconvenient changes in patterns of work), it can be a powerful force. Any attempt to change the way that things are done can be seen as an attack on the fundamental values and philosophies of the organisation, and as a threat to service quality and commitment to consumers.

We have found in our teaching, as well as in our work on this book, that health and community services staff can have difficulty accepting some of the basic features of the project method: the limited goals, the emphasis on concrete 'deliverables' and the importance of questions like 'will it be finished by the end of next month?'.

The idea of enhancing culture and climate may seem like a forlorn hope to embattled project managers and organisation leaders. Culture change may be difficult and sometimes painful, as Case 2.2 illustrates, but attention to culture is useful for two reasons. Firstly, even difficult and slow changes have to begin somewhere, and projects can make a

Case 2.2 New mission, old culture: a project manager caught in the middle

A branch of a national organisation focused on a common chronic condition had realised that they were failing to reach population groups with higher incidence of the condition and a greater burden of illness and disability. A manager with a strong background in working with disadvantaged communities had recently been appointed to the health care team, with responsibility for education programs, resources and other forms of support for people with the condition. She had been recruited partly for her capacity to lead a reform project aimed at achieving a greater focus and reach among those with the highest needs for support services.

She established a project steering committee, chaired by the CEO, and prepared a proposal for an overhaul of the way the health care team fulfilled its responsibilities, including tailoring its programs to single-parent families, to those with lower literacy skills, and to people living in rural and regional areas, including Aboriginal communities. She also proposed a change in the style of the organisation's publications and visual imagery to make it more inclusive and accessible. Other senior staff and particularly the CEO started to get nervous when they realised that the shift had implications beyond just the health care team.

Some of the existing health care team members were also uncomfortable, and one resigned as soon as he realised what the changes would mean for his job. The team manager took the opportunity to recruit a young educator who had transferable skills brought from experience in international development work.

The project proceeded, and gradually the team united behind the new manager and accepted the new challenges. Early outreach efforts to the target community organisations seemed to go well, and staff were gaining new insights into working with people of different backgrounds to their own as partners as well as clients. The board received positive progress reports and were strongly committed to the change, but the CEO was increasingly ambivalent about the project, could not relate to the new approach, and was uncomfortable interacting with members of the target communities. The team manager started to get really worried when the CEO asked her to divert some funding she had acquired to cover the cost of new resources for clients in order to cover a shortfall in the budget for another area of the organisation.

The team manager decided that she couldn't cross that line, and challenged the CEO on the ethics of his request. Things went downhill fast from there, and the upshot was a complaint about bullying, and finally a case in the industrial tribunal. It was too late for the manager, whose health was suffering, and she accepted a payout and left the organisation in a fairly bruised condition. The board sought and received the resignation of the CEO. They had realised that the changes they sought were going to require a more careful and thorough approach, because significant aspects of the organisation's culture were going to have to change. They set about recruiting a new CEO, and a few new board members (younger and more culturally diverse) to strengthen the base on which to build a different future for the organisation.

significant contribution to culture change. Secondly, the savvy project manager needs to see clearly, and work with and around, the cultural barriers they can't change.

People management and project skills

Project capacity can also be built through attention to the people side of organisations in two specific ways: in finding and keeping good project managers; and in embedding the skills of project management as part of the organisation's knowledge.

The importance of having the right staff is universally recognised. But this will not be achieved by placing people in project manager roles because they have a good idea and want to be the one to implement it; or because they are good at something else; or because you have nothing else for them to do and need to find them a job.

To avoid these problems, some organisations recruit project managers from outside, either as consultants or as temporary employees. This can work well but is not always a satisfactory solution—consultants can be expensive, they might not fit in with organisational culture easily, and they might not be very good despite their glowing references and marketing. The same applies to temporary project managers—by the time you find out that they haven't really got the skills you thought they had, you are halfway through the project. Careful attention to the skills needed for the project can help with selection. Those hiring consultants need to be clear on the priorities—where does the balance lie between generic project management expertise, knowledge of the organisational context, and project content knowledge? With clarity on these questions, at least those doing the hiring will know what they are looking for, and some consulting firms can offer project managers with specific skills to suit.

It may be more strategic to identify and keep good project managers within the organisation. Skills that are seen as valuable for project management such as communication, negotiation, facilitation, and change and conflict management are valuable for all managers. The temporary nature of projects, and particularly the timing of project funding, also means that organisations need to focus on embedding the learning and skills gained through their projects, and on retaining corporate knowledge. This can be difficult if project managers are contract staff who take the learning and corporate memory with them when their contracts end, a problem that can only partly be addressed through adequate handover and documentation.

The Project Management Office

Faced with an increasing number of projects being undertaken at any one time, many large health organisations are establishing a **Project Management Office** (PMO) to enable monitoring and standardisation of project activities. A PMO is a group or department within a business or agency that defines and maintains standards for project management within the organisation. The PMO strives to support, standardise and introduce economies of repetition in the execution of projects (Wikipedia 2018c).

The role and function of a PMO may vary according to the organisation's needs, but can include the following (Hobbs & Aubry 2007):
1. monitoring and controlling project performance
2. development of project management competencies and methods

3. multi-project management (the management of multiple projects)
4. strategic management of the project portfolio
5. organisational learning
6. executing specialised tasks for project managers
7. managing project customer interfaces (with vendors, government and other external parties)
8. recruiting, selecting, evaluating and setting salaries for project managers.

Bolles and Hubbard (2012) describe a range of PMO types, including:

- **Enterprise PMO:** ensures that projects align with the organisation strategy and objectives. These have the broadest remit of all PMO types, typically reporting directly to the CEO (or similar role), and having authority to make strategic and tactical decisions across all projects.
- **Divisional PMO:** provides support to projects for a specific business unit within an organisation; includes portfolio management, training, resource planning and project coordination.
- **Project PMO:** established for the duration of a single large project or program; includes administrative support, controlling, reporting and monitoring.
- **Project Management Centre of Excellence** (PMCoE): defines common project management standards, procedures, methods and tools to support project teams across an entire organisation; includes administrative services and training in process, methods and tools.

Projects in government departments

Government looms large in project management in the public sector, with central departments being involved at several levels. Their policies and programs generate and direct a lot of the project activity in service delivery agencies. They also conduct or commission a large number of projects as part of fulfilling their own responsibilities, and they, too, experience difficulties managing their project portfolios. Government is an area where the ideal of fixed goals and timelines is particularly hard to achieve.

Much of the work of staff in government departments can be defined as projects. The development of policies and standards, and the tendering of programs and services, are common examples. The processes of project definition and project approval have a political as well as a bureaucratic component, and the birth of projects may be particularly complicated in sensitive and newly emerging policy areas. Projects emerge and take shape from the interplay of political decision-making, interpretations at the governance level of the department, and the constraints of operational processes.

For many reasons, government departments tend to make extensive use of external consultants for major projects. Periodic reductions in the size of the public-sector workforce and the resultant loss of skilled people have made it harder for departments to contribute to policy development. Executives must often choose between 'treading water' (and thereby making little progress on major issues) or using outsourced intellectual capability. External players are seen as being more objective, while also potentially bringing the benefit of the transfer of skills to departmental staff.

In the rest of this book, we turn to the models and methods of project management that are the immediate influences on project success, and that we have argued are supported or constrained by the industry and organisational factors outlined above. But first, we want to apply the industry and organisational analysis to the question of project strategy: the decisions organisations make about what project opportunities to pursue, and how they manage their overall project effort. In the rest of this chapter, we present some criteria for use in selecting and approving projects—the organisation's 'project portfolio' is the sum of these choices.

The project portfolio

Health and community service agencies are increasingly taking an active approach to managing their project portfolios, and many have established practices for developing project proposals, setting criteria for their approval, ranking proposals against one another, selecting those to be approved (either for internal funding or to be included in bids for external funding), and resourcing and coordinating the resultant activities.

In larger organisations, these processes are generally applied to sets of potential projects that are seen to be truly competing with one another for endorsement and resources within a division or program (such as quality improvement or buying new equipment)—rather than at the level of the organisation as a whole. Some smaller organisations have a single system for ranking and approving projects, ensuring coherence and manageability through a comprehensive annual priority-setting process.

It takes time to develop open, predictable, rational methods for prioritising projects, but experience indicates it is worthwhile. How do organisations ensure that they invest in projects that are well designed and capable of delivering the desired results? The criteria for adopting projects into a portfolio will be unique to each organisation, and probably to the program or business area, and will change over time. Different criteria will get different weightings, sometimes overtly, sometimes covertly. Alignment with the organisation's strategic intent, and the feasibility of delivering the promised benefits are often espoused as the major criteria, but decisions can always be influenced by other agendas, or simply by a rush of enthusiasm. Having explicit criteria, and a rigorous process for applying them, is a safeguard against the influence of organisational politics or an excess of zeal, but not a guarantee. The ideas presented below are based on the project success model developed in Chapter 1, and are expressed as generic templates or principles that might be used in designing criteria.

Will this project help to achieve our strategic goals, directly or indirectly? This is really the starting point, but for many health and community service organisations the goals are so broad that even moderately skilled enthusiasts can make a case for almost anything under this criterion. Goal-setting theory tells us that specific goals are more motivating than vague general ones (Latham & Locke 1979), and in this case specific strategic goals are more useful as criteria. If the strategic directions statement or business plan is not specific enough, it can be the basis for a modified statement of strategic priorities for projects in the organisation, borrowing legitimacy from the main statement while making it more readily useful for project portfolio management.

There might be times when organisations decide to take on projects that do not fit clearly within their strategic directions, and there might be good reasons for doing so. For example, you might want to explore a particular care process to see if it is something you should be doing and whether it will fit with other aspects of your service. The strategic goals of the funders are also important, and sometimes it is worth being flexible on the alignment question in order to participate in important initiatives of governments and other funders. If this is the case, it is vital to be clear about why you are doing it and what you will do if it does or does not work out.

Does it fit with our culture and values, or what we want them to be—really? We have emphasised the importance of aligning the project portfolio with the organisation's strategic directions, but we have also noted the difficulties human service organisations often experience in moving in a coordinated way. Culture clash is a powerful source of some of these difficulties: 'Culture eats strategy for lunch' (attributed to Edgar Schein). We are not suggesting that projects that challenge the prevailing culture should always be avoided. Rather, we are saying that success is likely to be more difficult. Cultural factors need to be considered carefully, and the barriers to change identified, before a method for dealing with them can be factored into the project plan.

Another way of thinking about this is to consider the fact that many projects are focused on achieving improvement through changing the way operational processes work. Such projects occupy the 'white spaces' in the organisation chart (Rummler & Brache 1995); that is, they focus on processes in which typically several teams or departments are involved—and no-one is in charge. This is also the area where some of the 'unwritten ground rules' (Simpson and DuPlessis 2015) that encode the culture of the organisation are created.

It is worthwhile to check the project fit with the culture and values in two ways. Firstly, does the project, its goals and methods, sit well with the values we aspire to? And secondly, will this project encounter strong resistance because it cuts across some of the strongly held values or practices of the unwritten ground rules of the organisation?

If the answer to the second question is 'yes', then decisions must be made as to whether the project offers a good opportunity to challenge these values and practices, and how this might be done. The other option is to look for ways of avoiding the point where the clash of values occurs. It may be, however, that the culture problem is so strong that the project is doomed to failure and should not be taken on.

Is this a project or an aspiration? Hope is not a method—having a good idea, or a worthy aspiration, does not necessarily translate into a feasible project. Projects need both a goal and a practical method—they need to be clearly defined, concrete and achievable within a timeframe that can be reasonably estimated. Without a method, you may have a pressing problem or a great opportunity, but you will not have a project. The means of solving the given problem, or taking advantage of the opportunity, need to be clearly identified, feasible and available.

Is there a leader for this project—a sponsor who will make sure it delivers? Lack of leadership causes problems at two levels. The first is the level of the project team (see Chapter 8), but here we are focusing on the second—someone in a leadership position who is prepared to sponsor or champion this project, to be the person who will provide influence and access to needed resources when the team requires it. 'Top management support' is often cited in the project management literature as a make-or-break factor (for example, White & Fortune 2002). But the level and type of support that is needed will vary widely depending on the project and the organisation's structure and style.

Does this project require partners and, if so, is this feasible? Failure to recognise the external implications of projects is a common problem reported in the literature, including White and Fortune's large study (2002). Our informants spoke often of the need for effective partnerships to achieve many of the service development projects they had embarked upon.

The challenge is to recognise the need for partnerships in the early stages and to manage them well. Organisations that are more engaged with their environments and their communities, and which have established more robust relationships, are better placed both to see the implications and to move quickly to respond to them.

Do we have, or can we readily get, the skills to succeed with this project? Again, we are referring not only to project management skills, but also to the core competencies of the organisation—are we innovators or implementers? Do we have the basic technological know-how to support this project and its results? Are we in a position to work well with the intended client group, and with the key funders and regulators?

This criterion can also be used for consideration of the human resource questions—will this project provide good opportunities for the development of project skills and for career development?

Can we handle the resource requirements in a timely manner? This question is not simply about accurate estimation and securing the direct funding requirements of the project (See Chapters 6 and 7). The question here is about the capability of the organisation to mobilise the skills, staffing and management attention required to support effective project management.

If it succeeds, are the benefits worth the effort, and are the results sustainable? The project proposal will specify the intended benefits, and perhaps whether and when they will be able to be measured, but the question is whether the benefits justify the effort. Sustainability is a related important challenge, and one that is often deferred. 'We won't know 'til we get there' may often be true; and sometimes you need to demonstrate a successful approach in order to generate the conditions for acceptance and resourcing. But organisations should include consideration of this kind of project risk in their planning and decision-making.

Will this project contribute to our organisational learning and competence? Related to the theme of sustainability is the question of the potential for projects to contribute to the development of the organisation, its core competencies and organisational learning.

The 'which projects should we do?' checklist below summarises our analysis of project portfolio selection. It is necessarily generic— we suggest that individual organisations could refine the list to focus it more strongly on their unique considerations.

Checklist: which projects should we do?

- [ ] Will this project help to achieve our strategic goals, directly or indirectly?
- [ ] Does it fit with our culture and values, or what we want them to be—really?
- [ ] Is it a project or an aspiration?
- [ ] Is there a leader for this project—a sponsor who will make sure it delivers?
- [ ] Does this project require partners and, if so, is this feasible?
- [ ] Do we have, or can we readily get, the skills to succeed with this project?
- [ ] Can we handle the resource requirements in a timely manner?
- [ ] If it succeeds, are the benefits worth the effort, and are the results sustainable?
- [ ] Will this project contribute to our organisational learning and competence?

Summary

- The health and community services sector is strongly regulated, but also dynamic and constantly changing.
- There are four influences that shape project practice in health and community services: the role of government as regulators and funders, the extent to which projects are used as part of ongoing change, the tendency to overestimate what can be achieved and underestimate time and resources, and the influence of multiple empowered stakeholder groups.
- Government departments are deeply involved in project work, and experience a clash between the project management approach and the complexities and vagaries of government policy and bureaucracy. Governments are also an important influence on project agendas.
- There are four key factors that underlie the capability of organisations to succeed in project management: strategic direction, leadership, supportive culture and climate, and good people management (including building and maintaining project skills).
- With increasing numbers of projects being undertaken, larger organisations are establishing Project Management Offices (PMOs) that aim to support and standardise project work across the organisation, and gain the benefits of sharing knowledge and building capability.
- Based on evidence about project success factors, criteria for senior managers to use in choosing which projects to support can be specified. They can also be used by middle managers as a guide to how to pitch their project proposals.

Readings and resources

A practical approach to 'reading' organisational culture and climate:
Unwritten Ground Rules: www.ugrs.net/index_newlook.html
On engaging consumers:
Health Issues Centre Resource: www.healthissuescentre.org.au/subjects/list-library-subject.chtml?subject=24
On investment in eHealth:
Australian Digital Health Agency: www.digitalhealth.gov.au/
On project management methods and tools:
Axelos, 2017, *Managing Successful Projects with PRINCE2*, London: The Stationery Office

Project Management Institute (PMI), 2017, *A Guide to the Project Management Body of Knowledge*, 6th edn, Newtown Square, PA: PMI Inc
On the PMO:
PMO resource: www.pmi.org/learning/library/project-management-office-functions-support-6435

3

Understanding project management

Many of the people involved in new developments and innovation in health and community services, ourselves included, have learned by doing. That is, we have taken a rational approach to the planning and implementation of something new and used our managerial skills to ensure that it gets done. However, not all staff have had managerial training or experience, and we have found that the practice of expecting competent professional staff to be able to 'just do' project management is a common problem in the sector. Fortunately, this is changing, and there is a small but growing workforce of experienced professional project managers. Organisations are also now less likely to embark on innovations or changes that need to be managed as projects without realising it.

In this chapter we explain the foundations of project management as a method, and outline the emergence of careers in project management in the sector.

The terminology of project management

In the project management literature there are lots of acronyms—for example, PERT (**program evaluation and review technique**) and WBS (**work breakdown structure**)—and technical terms such as **Gantt chart**, 'close–out', 'go–live', 'benefits realisation', 'project scope' and 'deliverables'. It seems that project management has a language all of its own. The use of project terminology can be confusing—it is not necessarily consistent, and sometimes the terms are simply alternative labels for the activities that managers do as part of their daily work: setting goals and targets, deciding on strategy, working out tasks and responsibilities, and evaluating. However, the terms are helpful and are widely used by project managers and in project management literature. The glossary at the beginning of the book defines some common project management terms.

The project life cycle

The project life cycle—initiate, plan, implement and close—is a model that explains the normal progression of projects to completion (Kloppenborg 2009). Its use assists project teams to plan and monitor progress. But it is not usually a simple linear process. Instead, there may be two or more cycles of planning, implementation, evaluation and variation. Thus, the project life cycle is often used to refocus and reframe activities, and project management then includes a reflective learning process.

The first phase of the cycle, *initiate*, involves the identification of a problem or opportunity and some initial concept development and scoping. This is the 'good idea' stage. It is common for organisations to have a process for documenting and sifting these good ideas before any more detailed work is done. Those that pass this test enter the second phase, *plan*. This involves exploration and analysis focused initially on clarifying the goals; then on defining the scope (how big is it?); and finally on preparing a plan for how and when and by whom the project will be done, what resources are required and how success will be judged. The results of this stage are generally captured in a project plan, which may go through more than one version with checking and adjustments as details are added.

The third phase, which commences when the project plan is approved, is to *implement*. This is where the work happens, and all involved need to work together to get the tasks of the project completed. Managing this phase requires that the project's progress is tracked and corrected if needed, and that the tendency to drift into extra work or to change the original aims is also managed (sometimes through accepting change, sometimes by sticking to the plan). Implementation also includes ensuring that the costs don't blow out, that the defined deliverables are in fact produced, and that the needed data and information are collected and recorded.

The fourth phase is *close*, when the process of handover, or transitioning from the project to the new method or state, is completed. In this phase, final reports are submitted; all project documentation is completed and handed over; an evaluation of the project's success and the learnings is completed; and final communications are made, celebrations are held and thanks expressed.

Although these phases are presented sequentially, during the actual project several of the phases may occur concurrently or repeatedly (in projects with more than one stage, or as plans need to change). Information system projects and those involving software development will likely incorporate phases according to the **system development life cycle** (SDLC). The SDLC is a term used in systems engineering, information systems and software engineering to describe a process for planning, creating, testing and deploying an information system. The SDLC is not a method per se, but rather a description of the phases in the life cycle of a software application. These phases (broadly speaking) are investigation, analysis, design, build, test, implement, and maintenance and support (Wikipedia 2018d), but may differ according to the system development methods being used, such as **waterfall**, **Agile** or **Scrum**. According to Taylor (2004, p. 39), 'the project life cycle encompasses all the activities of the project, while the systems development life cycle focuses on realizing the product requirements'.

The use of repeated cycles of the project management method is diagrammatically represented in Figure 3.1.

Multistage projects

As well as having a life cycle, projects may be divided into more than one **stage**, to make a large or complex project more manageable, and sometimes because each stage has associated outputs or deliverables (that is, tangible, verifiable work products) (PMI 2017, p. 4). For example, a project that aims to acquire and implement a new information system for registering clients of a mental health service will have at least one '**go/no go**' decision point—that is, the time at which the organisation decides whether to accept the chosen system. Work before and after that point can be seen as two cycles (initiate, plan, implement and close) within the larger project or, in other words, as two separate stages. Other stages

Figure 3.1 Multistage project life cycle

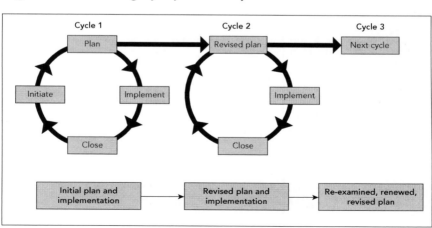

might also be required—for example, following technical installation and testing, it may be useful to manage the remaining implementation work as a separate stage of the project. There may be significant aspects of the commissioning process that require new planning, execution and closure (such as the conduct of staff training, the transfer of existing data and 'go-live' commissioning), which were unable to be planned before the system was tested.

As can be seen from this example, defining project stages and their outputs enables progressive decisions to be made about whether or not to move on to the next stage. This would normally take the form of a requirement for 'sign-off' (formal acceptance by the client or sponsor of the project) before the next stage could proceed. Many projects do not continue after the completion of a stage for a variety of reasons—perhaps they were found not to be feasible, or were not able to be completed within acceptable timeframes, or were simply not important enough to the organisation.

The number of stages and the activities or deliverables in each stage depend entirely on the project and the industry within which it is being carried out.

Examples of project life cycles

A generic statement of the project life cycle and two examples are provided in Table 3.1.

All projects involve the principal phases as described in Table 3.1, and certain phases might contain a greater number of steps than others depending on the nature and size of the project. Projects involving the procurement and implementation ICT can have a more complex life cycle than other projects—including several stages—but they still essentially use the same tools and techniques to achieve project success. This does not necessarily mean that other types of projects are any less complex to manage.

The examples in Table 3.1 demonstrate the rational approach to the project life cycle, but this way of thinking about the phases of a project can mask a whole series of practical problems and difficulties that may later emerge, particularly when projects require significant change. As we explore each of the major project activities and tasks, this issue of the rhetoric versus the reality of projects, and ways of dealing with the gaps between the rational approach and the 'shadow side' (Egan 1994), will be addressed.

Table 3.1 Examples of project life cycle phases

Generic project	Health promotion project	ICT project
Initiate: Feasibility or needs analysis. This can be called the feasibility, analysis, strategy, conception, proof of concept or discovery phase. This is the phase that basically works out what you want to do and whether you can do it.	*Initiate:* Rationale, community needs analysis, key stakeholder consultation, literature review, action research	*Initiate:* Research, project scope, business case, budgeting, acquiring capital funds, authorisation, finding a sponsor, specification development (technical, functional), planning of procurement process (expressions of interest), RFT (request for tender), vendor demonstrations, tender evaluation, contract with vendor, implementation planning study (undertaken by vendor), project initiation, planning workshops and functional, technical document production
Plan: Planning and design activities. This is sometimes referred to as the demonstration and validation, first build or preclinical deployment phase. In this phase you know what you want to do and you have to decide how you are going to do it.	*Plan:* Developing the plan, setting goals, objectives and strategies, defining tasks, timelines, resources, responsibilities and outcomes	*Plan:* Design of project management structure, technical architecture, product delivery, data migration, integration, implementation strategy, development, training strategy, testing strategy, issues and risk management strategy, benefits realisation plan
Implement: Production, second build, construction or development phase. This is the difficult bit—making it all happen.	*Implement:* Hiring new staff, training existing staff, procurement of equipment, preparing material, organising and conducting workshops, seminars and other project activities	*Implement:* Technical configuration, system configuration, system integration, system migration, software implementation, system testing (acceptance, user acceptance, regression), user training

Table 3.1 Examples of project life cycle phases *continued*

Generic project	Health promotion project	ICT project
		Go-live: Go-live schedule, operational readiness testing, process data migration, fix any rejected data, go-live support
Close: Turnover and start up, final or production and deployment phase. The product, deliverable or outcome is put into practice to see if it works. Evaluation is carried out to determine whether the project has met its aims, objectives and stakeholder expectations, and whether it did what it set out to do and is sustainable.	*Close:* Evaluation and review, often including a decision about whether to sustain the outcomes of the project as an ongoing part of the organisation's services or programs	*Close:* Transition from project status to support status, review outstanding issues, project review, closure, benefits measurement

Differentiating projects and programs

In the health and community sectors, there is a need to distinguish projects from programs or services. Projects are one-off activities with an end result (which may include trialling and refining a program or service). A program, on the other hand, is usually a service, intervention or set of activities that aims to meet a health or social care need. It may be ongoing, or have a defined operating period; it may also be a grouping of related services or interventions. Case 3.1 demonstrates how projects differ from programs in a community health service.

As shown in Case 3.1 below, when testing a diabetes management program (Healthy Eating and Active Living [HEAL]) over six months with a small participant group, HEAL is being managed as a project, to be evaluated during the trial and on completion. Once HEAL is offered routinely, it is no longer a project but a program that will be run regularly, using program management techniques to ensure that it remains effective and is delivered efficiently on a 'business as usual' basis. There are some real similarities between program and project methods, but it is useful to make the distinction.

The other use of the term 'program management' in the project management literature is to mean a group of projects managed in a coordinated way to obtain benefits not available from managing them individually (PMI 2017, p. 11). Program management is also used in a more general sense, to include both projects and ongoing business activities. For example, Roberts (2011, p. 14) refers to a program as:

> a management vehicle for progressing, coordinating and implementing an organisation's strategy, specifically by linking together an often complex combination of business activities and new projects, all of which are focused on the delivery of a defined business objective.

Case 3.1 Program and project in primary health care

Program: A community health service is planning to adopt the 'Healthy Eating and Active Living' (HEAL) program—an evidence-based type 2 diabetes prevention program—targeting people at risk of developing type 2 diabetes who live in the local government area. The HEAL program's main aim is to reduce the participants' risk of developing type 2 diabetes through lifestyle behaviour changes. The program helps them develop their skills, knowledge and motivation to achieve and maintain these lifestyle changes. The HEAL program runs over six months and is divided into two parts. Participants are supported and motivated to reach a weight-loss goal by adopting a healthy eating plan and taking part in moderate daily exercise. The program objectives include participants increasing their physical activity to five 30-minute sessions per week; developing a positive attitude to their own health; improving aspects of their diet (by 50 per cent); and improving their confidence in their ability to manage their health (by 60 per cent). Upon completion, participants are referred to local support networks to help them to maintain their improved lifestyle. The community health service is planning to run this program twice per year and to review it on an annual basis. Before implementation, the service would like to pilot test this program, to identify any implementation problems and to trial (for example) specific recruitment strategies and coaching methods.

Project: To recruit fifteen participants (aged between 45 and 55, and at risk of developing type 2 diabetes) for the HEAL program between May and October. The aim of the project is to test the program's capacity to reduce participants' likelihood of developing type 2 diabetes, by trialling and evaluating the success of the method in this setting. By the end of the six-month project, achievement of the program objectives by this group of participants will be measured to test whether HEAL can produce the intended benefits in this setting, and to identify any changes required for successful implementation of the HEAL program as part of the ongoing activities of the community health service.

Project management methods

The objective of using a project management method is to ensure projects are successful, through the use of tools and techniques that enable projects to progress in effective, disciplined and reliable ways. A project management method is essentially an approach that can be used to help conceptualise and understand the tasks of managing a project to success, and how and when to use project management tools. Using such methods does not guarantee successful outcomes, but success is less likely without them. However, choosing a project management method is not always a simple task.

Experienced project managers sometimes give the impression that the use of a favourite model or method is the only way for projects to succeed. But, in fact, there are several methods of project management in use in the health and community services sector. Many organisations use their own in-house tools and methods, or a hybrid of in-house and standard methods. While certain principles and methods are necessary for project success, in most instances there is no one best way, and no single recipe for success.

Examples of project management approaches commonly in use in health and community services include those based on PRINCE2® (Axelos 2017), **Lean Thinking** (used for redesigning or 'transforming' the processes of health care [Kovacevic et al. 2016]) and PMBOK® (PMI 2017). The use of customised in-house approaches is common, for reasons of conformity with the organisation's established practices and ways of thinking, and to simplify the task. For example, some organisations use the Plan, Do, Study, Act cycle popular in quality improvement for planning and designing relevant projects.

There is some variation in practice in different settings. Some government departments and authorities have adopted PRINCE2®, often with local modifications, and use it as a framework, a set of guiding principles for project management. Whether a model of project management is used can also depend on the source of funding. If the project involves a tender process or a consultancy, some standardised methods used by government may be stipulated as part of the funding arrangement, including methods of contracting, **tendering** and procurement, and rules of **probity**. For example, the Victorian government requires the use of the technique known as the **Investment Logic Map** as part of its business case template for some publicly funded projects (Department of Treasury and Finance 2017).

Examples of project management methods

Several proprietary project management methods are available, and three of the more recognised ones—PRINCE2®, PMBOK® and Agile—are reviewed below. Many other methods are available in a multitude of textbooks and manuals on project management, but they vary in their relevance to the health and community services sector. In the eHealth field, vendors often bring their own project management methods (such as Cerner's MethodM® implementation/service delivery model), and Agile project management is gaining proponents, in particular for projects involving information systems and software development.

PRINCE2®
PRINCE2® (PRojects IN Controlled Environments) is a structured set of components, techniques and processes designed for managing any

type or size of project (Axelos 2017). Originally developed for use in ICT, it has been mandated in the UK public sector and is widely used (and perhaps often simplified) elsewhere. The PRINCE2® method is an adaptable process-based model for the management of projects, and includes principles, themes, templates and tools. The philosophy behind the PRINCE2® model is that although every project is technically unique, by having a single, common and structured approach to project management the need to devise a specific approach for each project can be avoided.

PRINCE2® provides an overview of project management theory, as well as practical methods for thinking about how the project fits into the organisation, how to go about planning and initiating the project, and managing the stages of the project. The PRINCE2® package also includes templates that can be used as is or adapted—for example, a project brief, quality plan, business case, communications plan, risk log and end of project report.

A Guide to the Project Management Body of Knowledge (PMBOK® Guide)

Published by the US-based Project Management Institute (PMI), *A Guide to the Project Management Body of Knowledge* is a widely used reference that encapsulates generally accepted project management knowledge and practices, based on the American Standard for Project Management (PMI 2017, p. 2). The project management knowledge areas described in the PMBOK® Guide are: management of project integration, scope, schedule, cost, quality, resources, communications, risk, procurement and stakeholders. Rather than being a recipe book for successful project management, this publication is an excellent resource explaining theories and principles of project management, project processes and phases, and relevant tools and techniques.

The Agile approach

The Agile approach uses short development cycles called 'sprints' to focus on continuous improvement in the development of a product or service (Alexander 2018). Commonly used as an iterative approach to managing software development projects, it focuses on continuous releases and incorporating customer feedback with every iteration.

The method incorporates a range of tools and approaches, including sprints, daily standup (meetings) and scrum teams (tightly focused small teams committed to the achievement of sprints). Advocates argue that the Agile approach fosters rapid system development, innovation and team collaboration. More information is available at www.atlassian.com/agile.

Project management tools

Project management tools are used to assist project teams to achieve specific tasks. Common tools are Gantt and PERT charts and computerised scheduling and tracking tools such as Microsoft Project™ or Mac Project™.

Many organisations have their own standard tools and templates for project proposals, plans, communication, risk management, status and variation reporting, and some have implemented software to facilitate some project management processes, so it is useful to check what is available in the workplace. If this is not fruitful, it is worth looking a bit further afield—a vast amount of information about the tools and techniques of project management is available in other industries, especially in engineering or ICT fields, some of them more useful than others in the health and community services environment.

Project management is an art, not an algorithm, and requires knowing when and how to use tools and techniques (Kliem 2007). Many tools will be ineffective, regardless of where they come from, unless they are supported by strong management practices, including effective negotiation, communication, leadership, use of alliances and networks, and change management methods.

Digital project management tools and technologies

The general digital tools we use every day are also useful in project management, including videoconferencing, the internet, GroupWare and network database management systems, the local intranet, scheduling software, voicemail, messaging and email. Webinars, blogs and online learning tools also have the potential to add value as project tools.

Project management software packages are available to assist in the management of projects and in the establishment of an organisation-wide project management information system. But again, there is more

to project management than just using project management software—
it does not manage the project for you. The potential pitfalls in buying
and using project management software include:

- the purchased software may never be used
- the software may be used for limited functions—for example, as
  a drawing tool, or for timekeeping or budgeting
- overly sophisticated software may be too unwieldy and too large
  to be useful
- detailed training may be required to use the software effectively
- the project manager may become too involved in the software,
  to the detriment of the project.

Microsoft Project is a commonly used project management product
which enables the use of Gantt, PERT and critical path charts, milestones, project baselines, resource allocation and a work breakdown
structure. Unfortunately, training in the software is sometimes the only
training that would-be project managers receive. It is important, when
evaluating project management software, to have a good idea of which
tools would assist in the management of individual projects, and whether
there is a need for a management system for multiple projects. Project
management software, as with any other ICT application, needs to be
thoroughly evaluated in relation to the organisation's existing systems,
software and projects. The process of evaluation and implementation of
project management software is a project in itself.

The method or the tool?

There is a difference between a project method and a tool. The *method*
is the practice of the activity; the *tool* is the mechanism by which it is
achieved. For example, monitoring the project schedule is an important
method of ensuring timeliness, and the Gantt chart is a useful tool for
the task. It is easy to get carried away with an impressive array of tools,
but it is important both not to lose sight of the underlying method and
to choose the correct tools for success.

Some authors and managers believe that there is a technique or tool
to cover any project management situation. For example, Kliem (2007)
states that project management is all about tools, knowledge and techniques for leading, defining, planning, organising, controlling and closing
a project. Others firmly believe that a good manager is also a good
project manager; that project management is really a case of common

sense based on experience; and that special tools and techniques do not necessarily add value. Project management methods may also be seen as a hindrance because they are too mechanistic, or as being of limited value in dealing with health and community organisations because they are designed for other environments. The balance is probably somewhere in the middle, in that formal project management methods and tools have their place and are of particular value in some projects, but may bring their own project bureaucracy and cannot of themselves ensure project success.

Project management resources

In this section, we present a short guide to finding project management resources that can both assist project staff to skill-up quickly and assist students of project management to find their way around the literature. These resources, many of them available free in libraries and on the internet, include project management textbooks, internet sites, databases, journals, templates and professional organisations.

Project management textbooks

A number of practical and useful project management textbooks are available, featuring varying amounts of jargon and technical complexity. There are not many texts that explore project management in health and community services (hence the need for this book). The following are suggested as good all-round project management texts (mostly available as ebooks) that project managers (and students) might find useful when investigating project management theory or when initiating or managing a project:

- Heagney, J., 2016, *Fundamentals of Project Management*, 5th edn, New York, NY: AMACOM
- Kerzner, H., 2017, *Project Management Case Studies*, 5th edn, Hoboken, NJ: John Wiley & Sons
- Meredith, J.R. & Mantel, S.J., 2012, *Project Management: A managerial approach*, 8th edn, Hoboken, NJ: John Wiley & Sons
- PRINCE2® official textbooks at www. prince2.com/aus
- Project Management Institute (PMI), 2017, *A Guide to the Project Management Body of Knowledge*, 6th edn, Newtown Square, PA: PMI Inc
- Project Management Institute Inc.: Various textbooks on global standards grouped into 'Foundational standards', 'Practice

standards and frameworks' and 'Standards extensions': www.pmi.
org/pmbok-guide-standards
- Rosenau, M.D. & Githens, G.D., 2005, *Successful Project Management: A step-by-step approach with practical examples*, 4th edn, Hoboken, NJ: John Wiley & Sons
- Verzuh, E., 2012, *The Fast Forward MBA in Project Management*, 5th edn, Hoboken, NJ: John Wiley & Sons

Project management journals

The leading journals dedicated to project management theory and practice are:
- *International Journal of Managing Projects in Business* (Emerald ISSN 1753-8378) www.emeraldinsight.com/journal/ijmpb
- *International Journal of Project Management* (Elsevier ISSN 02637863) www.journals.elsevier.com/international-journal-of-project-management
- *Project Management Journal* (Project Management Institute and John Wiley & Sons ISSN 19389507) https://au.sagepub.com/en-gb/oce/project-management-journal/journal203528

Most professional and management journals also carry articles about project management in their specific areas from time to time. These include *Australian Health Review, Harvard Business Review, Health Care Management Review, Health Services Journal, Journal of Health Care Management*, and *Journal of Health Organization and Management*.

Project management organisations

There are a large number of project management organisations with helpful websites. Many are dedicated to training in project management, while others offer services and tools. The following are considered to be key resources in their countries of origin or beyond:
- Association for Project Management (the UK peak body): www.apm.org.uk
- Australian Institute of Project Management (the peak body for project management in Australia): www.aipm.com.au/home
- International Project Management Association: www.ipma.world/
- Project Management Institute (US-based): www.pmi.org

- Project Management Institute China (division of PMI): www.pmi.org/about/contact/china
- Project Smart 'Project Management Articles': www.projectsmart.co.uk/articles.php
- ProjectManagement.com (origins in the ICT industry): www.projectmanagement.com/
- The Project Management Center: www.infogoal.com/pmc/

Project management skills and careers

Achieving good project outcomes depends on good project management, and having the right person in this role is critical. While project management has a set of methods, the art lies in understanding what the project must achieve, and in being responsive to contingencies, open and flexible, intuitive and able to deal with crises. Of equal importance is the persistence to keep the project moving on.

Project management skills

Projects vary enormously in size and complexity, and the workforce involved can be large and sophisticated, or a single person. At small scale, a single project officer takes on the functions of both manager and team, frequently sharing the role of project manager with the person they report to. They usually need to negotiate with other staff for contributions of time, energy and support (and this is true for almost all projects in one way or another). So even sole operators of projects need to pay attention to coordinating the work of others and motivating their (virtual) team.

At large scale (consider, for example, the project of building and commissioning new facilities for a hospital and moving the services, people and equipment to the new site), project managers may have both an in-house team and a large number of external consultants and suppliers to manage. Clearly, the knowledge, skills and experience required for success will vary along the continuum of scale and complexity, but also according to the substance of the project.

Opinions differ about the importance of content knowledge for the project manager—that is, does it matter whether the manager has expert knowledge in the project's area of focus? For example, in a project that will amalgamate two pathology services, how important is it that the project manager has a scientific background? For a project implementing a new diabetes service, does the project manager need a clinical background? How important are general project management skills and experience in these settings?

Our experience indicates that content knowledge is a distinct advantage, and that working familiarity with the culture of the organisation and the professional groups within it is almost essential. But project management skills are also essential.

Our conclusion is that content knowledge should be defined fairly broadly. For example, for a project that will develop a clinical service, knowing the clinical environment and its culture and dynamics is important, but you don't need to be an expert clinician. For an ICT project, you need to understand the ICT environment, information systems (including knowledge of the software development life cycle) and technical concepts, but you don't have to be an expert programmer. On the other hand, where a potential project manager has great content knowledge and general management skills, but lacks project experience, some training, mentoring and support might bridge the gap. In large organisations, this expertise is sometimes available from the Project Management Office (PMO), the **project director**, or an executive with responsibility for strategy and innovation (and whose job involves significant project leadership).

When it comes to selection criteria and choosing the best person, the general principles for defining the required knowledge and skills for any job apply. Knowledge and skills should be specified in terms of competence or ability required rather than particular qualifications or backgrounds. Careful definition of the requirements, so that there is a balance between strong content knowledge and project management ability, is also important. General skills and knowledge requirements include some or all of the following:

- Leadership ability—in particular, creates and shares the vision for project success, and motivates the team and stakeholders.
- Discipline and drive—demonstrates application to the task, takes responsibility, is decisive, has the ability to work effectively at both strategic and detail levels.
- Excellent communication and interpersonal skills—talks to the right people, influences others, builds consensus, makes the project visible, negotiates, lobbies for the project, can manage conflict.
- Initiative and organisation—works independently, meets deadlines and ensures follow-through.

- Technical project management skills—has know-how and experience.
- Local knowledge—knows the working environment and has the ability to adapt tools and methods to suit.
- Analytical and reflective—keeps their eye on the ball, understands risks, can read situations, is flexible and responsive.

All of these skills, attributes, experience and knowledge add up to a tall order when it comes to finding a suitable project manager, and it must be said that much of what is required of a project manager is only gained through experience—of projects, of workplaces and of people. Finding good project managers, especially those with the skills (technical and 'soft' or people skills) to deal with complex or large projects, is not easy.

Of course, no matter how experienced, competent, enthusiastic and intelligent the person chosen for the job of project manager may be, they cannot expect to operate effectively without support and cooperation from senior management, staff engaged in the project and the organisation at large. Good project managers are not made or developed overnight. However, experienced line managers will already have many of the skills and attributes outlined above, and the skills of project management can be learned.

For small and medium size projects, we have seen some evidence that the strategy of developing promising project staff internally has greater long-term benefits than the option of buying-in project management skills. Some organisations take a long-term view, and work to develop a project management culture or to encourage project management thinking throughout their organisations. They also invest in both formal training and informal learning opportunities for key members of their staff.

Project management careers

In the wider health and community services industry, there is evidence of increasing demand for project managers and project officers. A scan of employment advertisements shows that there are many opportunities at all levels and in all areas of the health and community services sector for fixed-term project positions for those with industry experience and qualifications. Contract and project-based employment arrangements increasingly suit employers in the current funding environment.

There is also an emerging career structure for project managers. Larger organisations are establishing PMOs and appointing senior project managers to positions that require them to plan, acquire funding and coordinate a set of major projects. Sometimes these roles are undertaken by the senior planning and development officer for the organisation. Experienced health and community services project managers are also recruited by consulting firms to jobs that offer increasingly complex project management tasks and team leadership and management roles. In specialised areas such as EMR projects, project directors and managers are often able to move from one project to the next, deepening their technical and professional knowledge and their standing in the field.

A career in project management can involve a number of roles. A larger project may include several categories:

- team member
- group/team leader
- project officer
- portfolio managers, including technical, testing, change and training managers
- project director
- program manager.

There are many pathways to becoming a project manager in the sector. Practitioners build their careers on achieving notable success from early small local projects. Experience is one requirement; professional development and formal qualifications generally follow for those who decide to specialise.

Project management courses and professional development

Courses, training and professional development in project management are offered by universities, project management organisations, consulting firms, technical and adult education facilities, and registered training organisations. Project management education is available by distance education, online, on site and face to face, and there are a few tailored to the health and community services sector. There is no single recognised qualification in project management in the sector. This is mainly due to the fact that the majority of project managers gain project management skills and experience on the job. But it is also due to the wide range of projects that are undertaken—from building hospitals to implementing

EMRs to trialling new approaches to child protection or juvenile justice. However, there are certificate, diploma and masters level courses in project management available through universities and further education facilities that provide the relevant skills, as well as the credentialling that assists in career development. Most Master of Public Health and Health Administration Programs in Australia include project management as one of their core subjects. We suggest that those looking for training consult their employers, their professional associations or experienced project managers for advice, as well as their favourite search engine. The Australian Institute of Project Management (www.aipm.com.au/home) offers training and maintains an up-to-date list of project management courses on its website.

Summary

- An understanding of the meaning of project management is essential for anyone doing projects in health and community services.
- Project management has a unique language, but many of the principles are familiar to experienced managers.
- The project life cycle is a useful model for thinking about and managing the phases of a project. It can also assist project staff to refocus and reframe the project if necessary.
- There are a number of project management frameworks, models, methods and tools that are of assistance in understanding project management concepts and theories. However, no single approach or method can guarantee project success.
- Project management software can be useful—and there are many good products available—but it does not substitute for leadership and sound management.
- Skilled project managers are in demand, and there are many valuable resources available to assist project managers, including books, online resources, project management (PM) organisations, journals, seminars and courses.

4

The initiation phase: what do you want to do, and why?

Chapter outline

Where do good ideas come from?
Getting to project goals
Goals, purposes, problem statements and benefits
    Project goals and objectives
    What are objectives?
Project scope and strategies
Turning ideas into projects
    Participatory approaches to developing project ideas
Planning and analysis methods
    Needs analysis
    Implementation Planning Study (IPS) and other
      specialised methods
    Literature review: using the evidence
In praise of opportunism
Responding to grants and tenders
Offering project tenders
Summary
Readings and resources

This chapter explains the first stage of the project life cycle—turning good ideas into practical project proposals. We start with the question of where ideas for projects come from. The chapter then explains the key steps to be taken in developing an idea into a project proposal that can be used to seek support, funding and approval, using methods and processes that work well in health and community services. The chapter addresses the question of how to get support for your project ideas, and concludes with a discussion of submitting applications in response to tendered projects or funding rounds, and contracting projects to consultants.

Where do good ideas come from?

Projects generally emerge from an organisational or team need—to solve a problem or take up an opportunity—and a good idea about how to meet that need. In our work we find that good ideas for projects arise everywhere, and that the process of emergence and capture of good ideas varies with the size and nature of the organisation and its approach to innovation and development. It is often the leadership group who identifies problems that need a project-based solution and then commissions project work. This top-down approach has the advantage of senior management support and therefore better access to resources. However, if the project requires change in the processes of service delivery, it may be more difficult to get staff further down the hierarchy to own and support it (known in project management language as 'buy-in').

Good ideas also arise at other levels of the organisation. Discussions among colleagues are a common source—about problems that need solutions, or new ways of thinking about them—in team meetings, case conferences, at networking forums, or from seminars or conference presentations or in the staffroom. Sometimes projects emerge simply because someone thinks of a better way of doing something (or reads a success story from elsewhere) and lobbies decision-makers to test it out.

Other management activities, such as strategic planning or organisational needs analysis, often give rise to projects. Project ideas may be a result of external opportunities such as a new funding round, a government policy change, a call for tenders or a change in the law (for example, a new occupational health and safety or privacy requirement).

Good ideas, then, depend on organisational strategic directions, individual passion and sometimes serendipity, as well as funding opportunities and good timing. Whether such good ideas can turn into projects that eventually get implemented depends on further action.

Getting to project goals

The first step in taking a good idea and turning it into a project is to define the proposed goal—what do you want to achieve? How is your good idea going to solve the problem, meet the need or take advantage of the opportunity? Our experience in practice and teaching as well as research has taught us that one of the most challenging tasks in developing a project is defining the goal in a way that lends itself to implementation and achievement, as illustrated in Case 4.1.

People often have a passion for their work, and the energy and commitment to innovate, but if they are not clear on exactly what they

Case 4.1 From aspiration to project goal

Staff in a small community agency were interested in reducing tobacco smoking in young people in their region, and they felt that this could be a major project for their service. After some investigation and some hard thinking about the resources at their disposal, they recognised that the challenges of such a goal were overwhelming, and they found that they were unable to agree on realistic objectives or strategies. After further investigation of what was possible, they defined a project that involved working with the peak tobacco control body, and the schools in their community, to ensure that high school students in their area had access to skilled support during a major citywide campaign on smoking (based on television advertisements and an interactive digital package). Their new goal was 'to ensure that high school students in our community have access to skilled support for avoiding or reducing tobacco use through their schools and teachers'.

They had not let go of their aspiration to contribute to reducing the health consequences of smoking, but they had committed to a focused, achievable goal—the first building block of a successful project.

are aiming for when they begin, the project is in trouble from the start—without clear goals, it is almost impossible to design effective strategies.

In the early stages of a project, it can be difficult to take the step of turning a worthy aspiration into an achievable project goal, for many reasons. Sometimes it is simply lack of familiarity with the technical meaning of goals in project management, but it may also be due to conflicting priorities among staff designing the project or to problems in matching the team's goals to the requirements of a funding agency. Whatever the reason, the process of getting to a focused goal almost always forces greater clarity about strategies, timelines and the meaning of success. Now is the time, at the concept stage, to debate the need for the project, the evidence for effective responses, the project's relevance to the organisation or unit's strategic goals and the potential to gain allies and support. At this stage, debate about these issues can be enormously productive. Later on, when resources have been committed and movement towards the goal has begun, such debate can cripple a project's chance of success. Further on in this chapter, we explain how to use evidence and analysis to establish the value and validity of the goals—depending on the level of debate, you may need to gather the evidence early in the process.

Goals, purposes, problem statements and benefits

The general project management literature is clear that a project goal is a statement of what the project itself will achieve (Roughley 2009) expressed in concrete terms. But in health and community services, project goals are not always so clear, particularly when projects are the basis for testing or implementing health and social programs.

Project goals are not statements of the reasons why you want to do the project. They are statements of what the project itself will actually achieve, in response to the problems or opportunities that the project will address, as illustrated in Case 4.1.

That is, if the project is successful, the benefits will include fewer young people taking up smoking, and current smokers reducing or quitting their habit, with the proven long-term health outcomes that result. But the goal of the project is more modest. It will be achieved if the community agency succeeds in engaging with schools, teachers and students, and in offering skilled support and good resources to participants to the desired level (measurable as, for example, the number of students who quit smoking, or resolve not to start).

In contrast, for social and health *programs*, it is often important to start with a goal statement related to health or social outcomes (benefits). The outcomes are the purpose of the program, and are expected to be achieved if the program is successful and is sustained. Table 4.1 defines some important elements of the kind of analysis that gives rise to programs, and shows an example from the field of falls prevention.

These different frameworks can be confusing. The program approach may be required if your project is essentially about setting up or testing a social or health program. Clarity about the stages of decision-making and action can resolve the potential confusion. That is, the organisation can agree that the first stage should be making a decision as to whether to set up this program, based on a full analysis of its **program logic** (Taylor-Powell et al. 2002) or a similar model, including an assessment of needs. If the answer is that the program should be established, the work of designing a project to set it up can begin.

Project goals and objectives

One of the fundamentals of project management is the principle that you first decide *what* you want to achieve, then work out specifically *how* to do it. There is, of course, an interaction between the 'what' and the 'how'—people always tailor their goals according to their means as well as finding the means to achieve their goals. But the principle remains, and the staging of project development accordingly is important: be clear about what problems you are going to solve or what needs to be addressed and what you need to do; *then* agree on how and when you're going to do it; and *then* get on with it.

What are objectives?

Objectives, like goals, are statements of what you want to achieve, but at a lower level. If you are going to meet your goal, what are the main steps along the way—the parts that, taken together, will add up to achieving the goal? Project goals are achieved by fulfilling all detailed objectives. In other words, objectives are more specific and immediate progress or changes that must be achieved if the project goal is to be met. Objectives in turn form the basis for strategies, and hence the activities or tasks by which the project is implemented. Table 4.2 gives some examples of an aspiration (or reasons for undertaking a project, and potential benefits), a goal statement and a statement of objectives for two projects.

Table 4.1 Goal, objectives and strategies for a falls prevention program

	Definition	Example
Problem statement	A statement detailing the main types of needs to be addressed and/or key problems to be solved by the program.	High mortality, morbidity and costs associated with falls among residents of 10 high care nursing homes in a local council area
Program goal— anticipated long-term benefits	A statement about the broad long-term change (desired outcome) that the program is working towards. The goal is what you ultimately want to achieve, to address the stated problem.	The reduction of mortality, morbidity and costs associated with falls
Program objectives— anticipated immediate/ short-term benefits	Statements about specific changes needed for progress towards the goal. Objectives relate to the goal and are encompassed in the goal. They state what will be different as a result of the program and form the basis of strategies or actions.	• To increase at-risk residents' balance and strength by 20% • To reduce the incidence of falls by 50% • To reduce the incidence of fractured neck of femur by 50% • To reduce annual health care costs for falls by $500,000
Strategies	A plan of action designed to achieve the objectives that describes how you are going to get the changes you want. Strategies are implemented through a series of activities and are best when based on evidence.	• Implement a falls risk assessment method • Ensure all staff are competent in falls screening and prevention • Implement a falls monitoring system • Reduce falls hazards in the facilities

Table 4.2 Examples of aspirations, goals and objectives for two projects

Project A: Social connections in the south-east	
Aspiration	To improve the wellbeing of people with mental illness and their carers in our region
Goal	To design and establish a service to reduce the social isolation of people with mental illness and their carers in the south-eastern region of New South Wales
Objectives	• To adapt the successful New Zealand 'social connections' program for our service system • To establish a joint working group with carer and consumer representatives to identify practical methods to improve coordination and collaboration among relevant services • To trial the program in one suburb and measure changes in levels of social isolation among participants • To evaluate the results and seek in-principle approval to implement the service across the region • (If approved in principle), to finalise a plan for region-wide implementation, including source of staff and financial resources required, referral protocols and quality assurance for final approval by the Regional Executive
Project B: Surgical Admissions Pathway	
Aspiration	To provide better and more timely urgent and emergency care in a major regional hospital, by enabling urgent surgical patients who have been assessed elsewhere in the region to be admitted directly to surgical wards without going through the standard emergency department assessment and queuing processes
Goal	To introduce a Surgical Admissions Pathway for urgent patients straight to the receiving ward; and test its capacity to reduce the overall length of stay for those patients and its impact on ED waiting times for all patients
Objectives	• To design the pathway in consultation with representatives of all relevant staff • To gain approval for trialling of the pathway • To implement the pathway for a period of six months • To evaluate the impact on LOS and ED waits • To make recommendations to the Surgical and ED divisions for longer-term implementation

Note: Project B based on the work of Jason Cloonan (unpublished).

As the examples above illustrate, objectives are a more detailed statement that specifies what needs to be achieved in order to realise the goal. They identify the approach to be taken to achieving the goal, and can include targeted levels of coverage or completion. For projects that aim to trial health and social programs, there are many ways to work towards a clear statement of goals and objectives: they can be established collaboratively through 'brainstorming' exercises; more information can be gathered to assess alternatives; and past strategies within the organisation can be reviewed with the involvement of key staff, managers and other stakeholders (such as peer organisations or government departments). Later in this chapter, we identify other techniques for gathering and assessing evidence that might also be helpful at this stage.

For other types of projects, like the introduction of new ICT, or innovation to meet the National Emergency Access Targets, the goals may be effectively set by corporate headquarters or the health or human services department. The role of the project sponsor and manager is then to determine objectives and scope, and most of the methods outlined in this chapter could also apply.

Project scope and strategies

The next major step is defining the size and timing of the project and identifying what needs to be done to achieve the goal and objectives. Scope is a commonly used term for the definition of the reach of the project—what functions or systems are in or out, what target groups, what interventions and so on. If goals define the focus, scope defines the borders. Generally, scope starts very broad, and is progressively narrowed as the practicalities of the project, and the challenges it must resolve, become clearer during the planning stage. Scope is usually defined when questions of who, what, where, when and how have been answered, and the project can then be given limits.

In a project, strategies are what you do to achieve objectives (and ultimately, the goal) or how you go about it. Strategies constitute a plan of action designed to achieve a specific objective and contribute to the broader goal (Eagar et al. 2001). Each strategy consists of a series of activities. Good strategies are:

1. best when based on evidence of 'what works'
2. feasible to implement, and affordable
3. acceptable to stakeholders, and allow them to address their concerns

4. consistent with organisational culture (style, values and skill sets)
5. consistent with relevant policies (organisational, industry, government)
6. aligned with relevant government and organisational strategies
7. designed so that, taken together, they address the challenges the project is likely to face.

For large and complex projects, **feasibility studies**, **proof of concept** and **pilot studies** may be conducted to assess alternative strategies. Even in small projects, it is a good idea to check that the assumptions underlying the strategies are supported by the available data. It is remarkable how often projects are designed to use strategies that can't work, sometimes precisely because of the problem they are trying to solve. For example, if the problem is poor access to cardiology services, it probably won't work to design an alternative pathway for access that depends on cardiologists doing more work. This may seem like an obvious mistake, but it is a real example.

Generally, strategies can be designed to meet each objective in a project, as Table 4.3 illustrates for the projects introduced in Table 4.2. But in many projects, a single strategy (like a focus on engagement of relevant staff) will contribute to more than one objective.

Turning ideas into projects

Once the project goals, objectives, scope and strategies have been at least tentatively defined, much of the work has been done for an initial project brief. Many organisations in the sector have in-house templates or forms that enable staff with good ideas to formulate them into an initial proposal and seek in-principle support or approval to proceed to further development. These tools also aim to ensure that all the major questions are answered in a standard format.

The value of such an approach is, firstly, that staff are encouraged to articulate their ideas and think them through if they want to get support; and, secondly, that ideas can be assessed early on for fit with the strategic directions of the organisation and other important criteria. The **project concept brief** normally addresses (briefly) the following: a description of the problem or need or opportunity to be addressed and the potential benefits to be realised; the proposed project goals, objectives and strategies; the proposed timeline and possible resource requirements; and the relevance to the organisation's purpose and strategic directions.

Table 4.3 Objectives and strategies

Project A: Social connections in the south-east
Objective To establish a joint working group with carer and consumer representatives to identify practical methods to improve coordination and collaboration among relevant services
Strategies • Negotiate arrangements for carer and consumer representatives to participate in a working group • Establish and resource a 'key service working group' to allow regular structured networking opportunities within 3 months • Establish a web-based directory listing all support services in the south-eastern region for people with mental illness and their carers, and a method for service providers to provide updates, within 4 months
Project B: Surgical Admissions Pathway
Objective To design the pathway in consultation with representatives of all relevant staff
Strategies • Map the current processes of assessment, initial treatment and admission for the eligible patient groups; design alternative processes and prepare draft pathway document using a working group of relevant staff representatives • Consult broadly with staff and other experts on the draft pathway and refer suggested changes to the working group for assessment, amendment of draft and sign-off

The templates or forms are variously called a 'project proposal', 'project brief', 'project scope' or 'project definition'. They sometimes vary between different parts of the organisation, to suit different kinds of projects. Well-designed templates can be a valuable way of guarding against sloppy thinking, as they assist proponents to identify whether their vision or good idea can really be translated into practical action. This tool can also be used by senior management to get an overview of what projects are being initiated within the organisation, for the purposes of prioritising, and also to monitor and manage the organisation's project portfolio. Like any tool, project templates can become bureaucratic impediments if they are poorly designed or inappropriately used. The project proposal template (Template 4.1) at the back of the book is designed to prompt proponents to think through the precise goals and deliverables, the required resources, the costs and benefits, the support from key stakeholders and the major components of work that will be required to take the project to successful completion.

If you are commencing this step, it's important to be realistic and to ensure that your project meets the organisation's criteria for support—not all good ideas survive the development and approval processes. The criteria in Chapter 2 for use by decision-makers in assessing project proposals can be turned around and used as a guide for those preparing project proposals to give them a better chance of getting approval. We suggest that staff preparing project proposals consider the following tips (not all of which might apply to any single project), and ask whether the project proposal measures up:

- Relate the project to achievement of the organisation's *strategic goals*, directly or indirectly.
- Demonstrate (or imply) *good fit with culture and values*, existing and desired.
- Demonstrate the *capability* of the organisation to undertake the project and that required *skills* are available (or can easily be acquired).
- Write a *practical project plan* that can be seen to be feasible.
- Understand the high-level costs and resources required.
- Marshall the available *evidence* that supports your idea (especially evidence that demonstrates the importance or urgency of the project, such as aspects of the changing health and social context and future policy or reform directions).
- Make sure the logic for your choice of *sponsor* for the project is clear and that any ruffled feathers are soothed.
- Deal with any *alliances or partnerships* that might be needed.
- Make sure the *resource requirements* are manageable and well timed, and that the project cost is justified by the potential benefits.
- Explain how the *results will be sustained*—that is, how the project outcomes can be embedded and continued in ongoing operations.
- Demonstrate how this project will contribute to *organisational learning* and competence.

These tips highlight many factors that can affect the chances of approval and support for project proposals. For example, management culture and culture of the organisation can be critical. If management is ambitious and proactive in trying out new ideas or service expansion, good project ideas will have a higher chance. This is not something that project proponents can change, but it is helpful to take these factors into account in shaping your project proposal. Timing, availability of resources and priority-setting are also important.

In many cases, it takes persistence and belief—and commitment to achieving a high standard in the project—to get the project off the ground.

Participatory approaches to developing project ideas

As illustrated in Case 4.2, in health and community services it is sometimes possible for project ideas to be developed in a collaborative, participatory way. It is also good practice to ensure that consultation with stakeholders is carried out early.

Case 4.2 Using participation to develop project ideas

A large health service was advised of a funding program that had very clear objectives and addressed an issue that was a high priority for the organisation. The whole organisation was invited to identify potential projects or initiatives using a brief proforma designed to collect good ideas while minimising the burden of writing the initial proposals. About 300 submissions were received.

A workshop with over 50 participants, including consumer representatives and other external stakeholders, went through a process of bringing the 300 down to 12, with a great deal of grouping and melding of ideas through discussion. A 'village marketplace' was created through which people were able to add value or combine ideas, with ultimate ranking of projects by all 50 participants, using a polling app on their mobile phones or on tablets. The top 12 projects were recommended to the executive, and 11 of them were approved for submission.

While this process consumed a lot of energy, it generated a set of ideas that were well tested and broadly supported, with an overt, transparent process. The executive believed that the process was worth it for the organisation for several reasons, one being the need to ensure broad support for the projects that were ultimately implemented. Another was to establish a collection of 'good ideas' that might be suitable for other funding opportunities.

Planning and analysis methods

Major projects often require detailed analysis of needs, costs, evidence of effectiveness etc., and there are many models and approaches. Sometimes, the information these methods contribute is needed as part of the initiation phase, or they can be done later as part of detailed planning. Three important analysis and planning methods commonly used in projects in the sector—**needs analysis** (or **needs assessment**), **Implementation Planning Studies** and literature reviews—are explained below. Not all projects will warrant the use of these methods, which can be time-consuming and costly, and require some technical knowledge and skills. However, if the project is complex or large in scale, these steps can be critical to test the merits of project ideas, and provide evidence for decision-making.

Needs analysis

The concept of needs in health and community services (and other areas of public policy) is used to determine the focus of interventions, services and programs. That is, services are seen to be worth funding because they can demonstrate that they are effective in meeting socially determined needs (that is, they produce the intended outcomes). The goal of needs analysis (or needs assessment) is to develop an understanding of the health or social problems experienced in communities by a particular group or population, and therefore the type and volume of services that are required. Needs analysis is undertaken in order to identify the sorts of interventions or strategies that can solve those problems and address those needs (Eagar et al. 2001; Royse et al. 2006; Royse et al. 2009).

Bradshaw's classic typology of needs (Bradshaw 1972a, 1972b) summarised in Table 4.4 specifies different ways of thinking about and measuring needs.

A good needs analysis can be a critical step to turn a good idea into a project, and it can also be a project in itself, depending on scope and complexity. As always, it is important to be very clear about the purpose and scope of the needs analysis; its intended users and what kind of evidence they will find convincing; as well as what will be acceptable and convincing for consumers, community and perhaps other stakeholders, like the local government authority.

Table 4.4 Bradshaw's typology of needs

Felt Need	What people experience as need. For example, pregnant women may feel the need for more information on childbirth and potential complications.
Expressed Need	An actual request for services or programs—a felt need expressed in the form of demand for services (people seeking the service) or through community action. For example, the need for a place to exercise in a local community may be expressed as a demand for exercise classes or the use of a gym. Long waiting lists at the local GP clinics are a form of expressed need for more GPs to work in the area.
Normative Need	Expert or professional views on what is needed, determined on the basis of research, professional opinion, value judgements or established standards. For example, the advisable levels of fluoride in water, or the daily recommended allowances of nutrients in foods, or accepted standards that specify the amount of open space for a given population.
Comparative Need	Level of need is inferred by benchmarking against the volume of services or programs in comparable settings. For example, by comparing access to supportive care and education for patients with diabetes in different geographic locations.
Latent or Unmet Need	Usually seen as a gap between known levels of need and actual take-up or availability of services or programs. For example, the difference between the number of diagnosed diabetics in a region and the number who access care; or the gap between demand for emergency admissions and the capacity of the local hospitals. This measure is useful for predicting the level of potential demand for services when designing new facilities.

Defining scope and focus of needs analysis

Well-designed needs analysis enables a systematic step-by-step approach to identifying and collecting relevant data and information. The first step is specifying the needs analysis questions. This may involve consideration of the following:

- Does the problem affect a particular population, community or group, especially a group that is disadvantaged in other ways?
- How prevalent is the problem—how many people experience it?
- How severe is it—does it cause serious debilitation or minor inconvenience?

- What is the service system capacity?
- What barriers and obstacles to change exist?
- Is this a study to argue for additional resources, or for the reallocation of existing resources to improve equity, or for reallocation of resources between different types of responses for the same need (for example, prevention versus treatment), or between different types of needs?
- Are there known effective interventions that should be included among the possible service responses? (Hawe et al. 1990)

It is very important to develop the right questions to assist with the needs analysis design. Note the two questions below and the different kind of investigations, scope and results that they imply.

- Needs analysis question 1: What are the gaps in follow-up services at City Community Health Service for patients who have completed chemotherapy treatment within the previous six months?
- Needs analysis question 2: What are the specific needs of the patients (who have completed chemotherapy within a six-month period) that could be addressed by developing an integrated referral pathway between City Hospital Cancer Service and the City Community Health Service?

Limiting the scope, and focusing the questions, is important not only for managing workload but also to minimise the risk of raising false hopes or identifying issues and problems that are well beyond the scope of the organisation to address.

Gap analysis

As well as information about the number of people involved, information about gaps and potential capacity in the available service system—**gap analysis**—may also be needed. The knowledge that current capacity is not adequate for current or predicted increases in demand can be used as the basis for deciding whether new services or service models are required, or simply the improvement of existing services. That is, could the (potential or actual) gap be solved through more efficient services, through different kinds of services or through bringing together the responses of different service providers?

For example, local Aboriginal and Torres Strait Islander people with cancer may be diagnosed later in the course of their disease than the general community, and the treating clinical staff might initiate discussions about the reasons for this and what could be done. Equally, community leaders may speak up and ask for changes in the way that members of the community are able to approach care providers or in the location and style of care. This kind of problem requires both genuine engagement of service providers and community representatives, and good use of data to understand the causes and potential solutions, and their costs and benefits. Community representatives will have the best insights into the reasons why patients seek care later, or are less well served by local health care providers when they do seek care. There are four characteristics of current services that should be examined—awareness, availability, accessibility and acceptability—before decisions are made as to whether this is a case for a service improvement project or for new interventions or models of care. Measuring a gap in services to address the identified needs and the capacity of existing services to address predicted increased needs is as critical as measuring the identified needs.

Needs analysis methods
Once the needs analysis questions have been finalised, methods for collecting data and information can be decided upon, with priority given to reliable sources that can provide meaningful and valid answers to the questions. Data can be from secondary sources (that is, already existing data collections, perhaps requiring new analysis) or from primary sources, which usually means people. Table 4.5 gives examples of secondary and primary data and ways they are generated.

Organisations also conduct needs analysis for other purposes, such as analysing the need for a human resource development program. The needs identified through such a process may lead to training and staff development activities, but they typically also identify other types of needs—for example, to overhaul the way work is done, the way jobs are structured or the arrangements for staff car parking. Any of these identified needs might require the development and implementation of a project. And, if so, the detailed data gathered as part of the needs assessment will be a vital input to the project definition.

Needs analysis process
The usual steps involved in completing the needs analysis process are illustrated in Figure 4.1, using the case of a care or service need.

Table 4.5 Data types

Primary sources, requiring interaction with human subjects	Secondary sources
• Focus group discussion • Community forum and consultation • Blood tests, weight measurement, fitness tests • Survey—email, web-based, telephone, written • Qualitative personal interviews • Observational studies • Case study	• Publicly available data from official collections (e.g. AIHW); population data including demographic data, social and health indicators etc. • Epidemiological data, such as disease distribution and onset • Service data, such as numbers of patients treated and level of service provided, waiting list and waiting times including 'did not attend' rates • Agency data collections on activity (e.g. routine clinical or quality indicators, client records of attendance, admission, demographic details etc.) • Organisational and administrative data (internal or external) • Documentation (project journal/diary, log, progress reports; agency policy manual, plans, agreements, minutes) • Data already collected by other projects using the methods in the left-hand column of the table

Figure 4.1 Needs analysis process

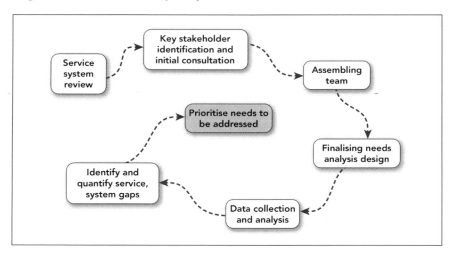

Needs analysis report

The production of a needs analysis report is the final step in needs analysis. A needs analysis report is typically structured along the following lines:

- background and introduction
- purposes of the needs analysis and needs analysis questions
- needs analysis design and plan
- key findings (needs, problems, gaps, tested and possible interventions, feasibility and prioritisation of tested interventions in the specific context and so on)
- discussion of findings and recommendation of the best interventions or solutions for further action
- conclusion.

Needs analysis often results in a large amount of information, most of it very valuable, which can make it a challenge to prepare a succinct report with a clear summary of the findings and conclusions and a limited number of recommendations. This is where a tightly defined and limited scope of the analysis—specified at the beginning of the process—pays off.

Implementation Planning Study (IPS) and other specialised methods

Several planning methods commonly used in ICT and information system projects when implementing large, new, complex or untested technologies or systems are outlined below.

Implementation Planning Study (IPS)

An IPS may be conducted prior to ICT or information system implementations (or contract signing), to identify and understand the solution to be implemented, the context and requirements of the implementing agency, and confirmation of the implementation scope and approach. Most commonly conducted in partnership with the software or technology vendor, the IPS typically involves a series of workshops covering: solution demonstrations and requirements, system integration approach, infrastructure/technology, data migration, training, testing and change management. An IPS report is usually delivered by the vendor, summarising the IPS activities, findings and decisions, which then informs the project plan.

Feasibility, proof of concept and pilot studies

One or more of these methods can be used prior to project approval or in the first stage of a multistage project to assess the practicality of a proposed plan or method where there is significant uncertainty regarding the implementation solution, project deliverable or an untried technology or model of care. A feasibility study is used to determine the viability of a method, approach or idea, to assess technical, legal, economic, operational or scheduling feasibility (Mukund 2017). A proof of concept (POC), commonly used to assess software capability, is a small exercise to test the design idea or assumption. The main purpose of developing a POC is to demonstrate functionality and to verify a certain concept or theory that can be achieved in development (Singaram & Jain 2018). A pilot study, pilot project or pilot experiment is a small-scale preliminary study conducted in order to evaluate feasibility, time, cost and adverse events, and to improve upon the study design prior to performance of a full-scale project (https://en.wikipedia.org/wiki/Pilot_experiment).

Literature review: using the evidence

There is an increasing acceptance in health and community services that decisions, policies and practice should as much as possible be based on, or at least informed by, evidence. Following its initial establishment in the field of medicine, the concept of **evidence-based practice** (and evidence-informed policy or decision-making) has now been largely accepted as a guide to policy development and health service management (Cookson 2005; Head 2010; Kovner & Rundall 2006; Shortell 2006).

For project proposals, this increasingly means referring to the relevant published research and policy documents, as well as to other more informal (but valid and reliable) sources. Evidence is not limited to peer-reviewed scientific studies (Kovner & Rundall 2006; Lavis et al. 2005; Liang et al. 2011). It includes:

- quantitative and qualitative research studies
- internal data, including reports, consultancies, evaluations and performance data
- examples of '**best practice**' in similar organisations or fields
- policy and management reviews, including auditor-general reports
- expert opinion from acknowledged leaders
- information about stakeholder or consumer preferences (empirical or expert-opinion-based).

Thus 'evidence' is a broad concept. The search for and analysis of evidence is generally known as a literature review.

Literature review is a process of evaluating relevant information found in the literature and should describe, summarise, evaluate and clarify the evidence (Aveyard 2010). All work included in the review must be read, analysed and evaluated for reliability, validity and applicability. That is, the quality of the evidence should be appraised (i.e. methods of data collection and analysis, interpretation of data in the specific context, and relevance to practice). Literature review can be an effective way of defining a problem; finding the current thinking on a subject; or assembling the evidence of effectiveness for a new method or technology, intervention or service. Literature reviews can assist agencies to avert misguided or even harmful projects that fail because they either do not meet a need or suffer from serious technical flaws in the way they are carried out. In other words, literature reviews can provide the evidence for decision-making about whether and how a project should proceed.

Conducting a literature review: finding the evidence

The first stage in a literature review is defining the subject area and knowing what you are looking for (which may be at least partly defined by the project proposal). The second step is finding the available evidence, beginning with defining search terms (the key words that identify the area of interest) and what kind of sources will be used, and setting time-period limits on the search. Literature searches generally use electronic databases to find journal articles, which requires access to a reference library. Most databases will have their own lists of keywords to help you search. Some valuable databases include ABI/Inform, EconLit, ProQuest, Emerald for business and management, CINAHL, PubMed and MEDLINE (Ovid). Google Scholar can also provide a good place to start. One of the easier and more efficient methods is to search within the websites of journals that publish relevant topics. The starting point might be obvious—a journal that is focused on the health problem or intervention or business process that the project will address. 'Snowballing' (going to the other journals that have published papers cited [i.e. referenced] in the ones you've already found) is another useful method. Search filters are even easier to use (see www.flinders.edu.au/clinical-change/research/flinders-filters/ for an explanation), but they are not available for all topics. For example, the filter for palliative care is Care Search (www.caresearch.com.au/Caresearch/Default.aspx); and for Aboriginal and Torres Strait Islander health, see the Lowitja Institute's LIt.search (www.lowitja.org.au/litsearch).

Journal articles and academic papers are valuable sources because they are subject to a peer review process intended to ensure intellectual rigour, and can be more current than books. Sometimes, a search will find a recent published review of the literature, which can save the searcher a lot of time. Research papers generally report on discrete research projects with clear aims and objectives, methods and analysis of results. The difficulty with journal articles is that sometimes they, too, are reporting on material that is a few years old. They can also be very technical and difficult to read and understand. Readers sometimes find that the problems investigated and presented in the articles are not of great interest to practitioners, and that the articles create more questions than answers. Moreover, findings and suggestions may not be sensitive and applicable to the local context in which the projects operate (Liang & Howard 2011).

Another key source of information is the **grey literature**—research that is unpublished or not formally published, and other sources such as government reports and websites. Examples of grey literature include policy statements and issues papers, conference proceedings, theses and dissertations, research reports, market reports, working papers and progress reports, maps, newsletters and bulletins, and fact sheets. This information may be circulated via your professional organisations and networks, and within the organisation where you work, or found on government and 'think-tank' websites.

Data and reports generated within your organisation can be particularly valuable, because they are current and local, and offer insights into both the needs of the relevant patient/client group, and the interventions or approaches currently in use. Being unpublished does not mean poor in quality. Much grey literature is of high quality and value, and is often the best source of up-to-date information on certain topics that may not yet have been widely studied. Using a search engine to find websites of government departments, professional institutions and non-government organisations is the starting point for accessing the grey literature. However, websites may have purposes other than to provide objective information. Their biases and their integrity need to be checked.

Finally, the thing to remember in literature searching is the importance of organisation—taking notes, keeping records (not only of the source but also of details such as page numbers for easy reference later), highlighting important concepts and capturing interesting ideas and potentially useful quotes. There are several software programs (for example, Endnote™) designed to make it easier to record and cite references.

Making sense of what you find

The search of literature will probably unearth many references and sources well beyond the scope of the project. Some will be obviously not relevant when you read the title and the abstract, and can be set aside; others will have to be read through to find whether they are relevant. Even if the paper is interesting, its quality and relevance still need to be assessed—that is, you need to critically appraise the evidence, and that requires some skill (Liang & Howard 2011). The essence of the process is to read each relevant paper, summarise the method and findings in a paragraph or two, and then write a few sentences summing up the impact of the results of the research or policy analysis. The research centre 'Health Evidence', located at McMaster University in Canada, has developed useful resources including a standard step-by-step guide and forms to guide health professionals in searching and in assessing the quality of research (available at www.healthevidence.org/). The Cochrane publication on 'how to grade the quality of the evidence' (Ryan & Hill 2016) also provides a practical step-by-step guide for making judgements on quality of evidence.

After finding and assessing relevant evidence, the next stage is to tell the story of what you have found. This requires integrating the learning or the main findings from the sources you have read, and writing the answer to the 'so what?' question—that is, taken together, what does this literature mean for the scope, focus, design or conduct of the project (and the benefits or use the organisation may make of its results)? Thus the literature review may help to set the parameters for the project as well as establish what is known about the topic. The literature review should inform the reader about the weight of the available evidence, as the basis for your argument as to why your project is essential and/or valuable, and why it should be approached in a particular way.

In praise of opportunism

We have focused in this chapter on the need to test project ideas for feasibility and relevance to strategic directions, and have advocated creative thinking and careful choices. However, there is also a place for opportunism, for several reasons. Sometimes an organisation needs to get runs on the board or build capacity and profile. Governments also respond to political issues, which may create opportunities. For example, if media attention is drawn to a problem that becomes a burning community issue—such as the use of drugs or inhalants by teenagers—governments will often respond by setting up a task force or establishing a project funding line to address the problem. Success then depends on the competence of project proponents to sell their good project ideas to the right people.

Responding to grants and tenders

In addition to seeking funds internally from the organisation, potential external funding sources should be considered at the early stage of conceptualising project ideas. Seeking and securing funding is a skill in itself. There are sources of funding for projects for health and community service agencies, each with different criteria and requiring different approaches. Governments are important funders of projects, usually via a tendering or submission process. Potential project funds can also come from non-government sources such as trusts, foundations, charities and public donations.

When seeking external funds to support your project, the quality of the project proposal or funding application is critical. If resources allow, organisations sometimes contract consultants to assist with developing and writing funding applications.

A tender is an offer submitted by interested bidders (organisations that apply or 'bid' to win the contract) to the agency commissioning the project (sometimes called the 'purchaser'), usually in response to a 'request for tender'(RFT), also known as an 'expression of interest' (EOI) or 'call for tender' (CFT). Some governments have promoted the competitive tendering process in order to obtain competitive pricing for the provision of services. Hence, there are many opportunities for organisations to bid for and win contracts, often for ongoing service delivery, but also for projects. Government RFTs are advertised widely, both in the news media and on government websites, along with information about tendering policies and guidelines (for information on competitive tendering and contracting by government, see www.pc.gov.au/inquiries/completed/public-service-tenders-contracts/48ctcpsa.pdf).

There are two distinct reasons for responding to a tender. Firstly, it may offer an opportunity to obtain funding for a good idea that has been under consideration for a long time—or for a variation of it. The other scenario is a more opportunistic one: a tender appears for something that has not been previously considered, or is perhaps not part of the agency's strategic directions but seems to bring other opportunities—and so a bid is made.

The questions and tips below are designed to help with the process of deciding whether to respond to a tender:

- Consider who is commissioning this project and why. Do you know what they are looking for?
- Do your homework, and use networks and contacts to find out as much background as possible.
- Always read the project brief/tender specification or funding guidelines carefully, and always follow the instructions.
- Make sure you have the relevant and up-to-date evidence to argue the importance of your project.
- Remember the application is for them, not for you—answer every question and respond with what they want to hear.
- Consider whether you are trying to fit one of your projects into someone else's project. If so, it might be difficult to achieve your aims (or even put in a successful bid).
- Make sure your tender bid (or EOI) is realistic in terms of time and cost.
- Consider whether the organisation has the necessary skills to carry out this project.
- Consider whether the roles and responsibilities are clear.
- Consider whether you have the support of senior management

Government contracts can be fierce about intellectual property (IP). Consider whether you will generate new IP or use your existing IP. If so, can your IP rights be protected?

Remember, the organisation that has tendered out this project has done so for a reason—which was not to give you the opportunity to finance one of your pet ideas.

Offering project tenders

For some organisations, projects usually mean engaging consultants, either through a tendering process or directly engaging a particular company because of their successful track record.

Deciding to tender out a project can be a tricky decision, given the challenges of preparing good specifications, and because of the tender process itself. Before putting out a project for tender, it may be useful to consider the following:

- Why is there a need to tender out this project? Is it because it is cheaper? Is there a lack of skilled staff? Or is it because the problem is best solved by an independent outsider with specific technical expertise?
- What kinds of people are needed to carry out this project? Can an external contractor feasibly achieve the required deliverables and outcomes?
- Are the skills and resources needed inside the organisation to manage the contract available?
- How long is it expected to take, and what will happen if it takes longer?
- How much should it cost?
- Are there any hidden costs to the organisation that have not been budgeted for?
- Is there an allowance for the costs of contract management, and of responding to the consultants' needs for information and access to staff?
- Are the required roles, responsibilities, accountability and monitoring methods clearly described?
- How will this project be evaluated?
- Have any IP issues been identified and can they be resolved satisfactorily?

Essentially the tender process involves a number of steps, all necessary to ensure the best possible outcome and to fulfil the organisation's obligation to treat all bidders fairly. Key steps are:

- development of specifications for the project
- preparation of a request for tender (RFT) document
- call for expressions of interest and tenders
- establishment of a process for responding to queries from tenderers
- receipt and evaluation of tenderers' submissions
- notification of successful and unsuccessful bidders
- negotiation of the contract
- signing of the contract.

Public sector organisations are usually required to advertise tenders for projects with costs over a specified dollar amount, and usually they are advertised on websites and sometimes in newspapers. The tender process must follow the principles of probity (the integrity of the tender process), which include fairness, impartiality, transparency, security, confidentiality and compliance with legislative obligations and government policy.

The discipline imposed by the tendering process can be helpful in forcing clear specification and adherence to the project plan. However, it can also cause problems when genuine contingencies arise and specifications or methods and timelines need to be changed.

Summary

- Ideas for projects originate from both within and outside the organisation, with many instigated by government policies or funding.
- Ideas for projects can be captured, evaluated and progressed using both formal and informal processes—for example, by using an 'ideas sheet' or a project proposal document.
- Participatory approaches to project development are more likely to enable effective stakeholder engagement, and can help to ensure the project is well designed.
- Projects need clear goals, objectives and strategies. Effort put in to getting them right in the early stages will pay off when detailed plans are developed, and implementation begins.
- Getting the project to 'in-principle' approval at the concept phase may require background work or research, or other pre-planning activities. These methods help to ensure that the need for the project is established, that it is based on good evidence and that it represents good value for money.
- Projects are often made possible by funding bodies who offer grants or invite organisations to submit tenders. Applying for funding involves significant work, but success is more likely if submissions and tenders are closely matched to the funder's requirements and preferences.

Readings and resources

On conducting a literature review and using evidence:

Aveyard, H., 2010, *Doing a Literature Review in Health and Social Care: A practical guide*, London: Open University Press

Fink, A., 2010, *Conducting Research Literature Reviews: From the internet to paper*, 3rd edn, Los Angeles, CA: SAGE Publications

Health Evidence at McMaster University: www.healthevidence.org

On economic evaluation:

Drummond, M.F., Sculpher, M.J., Torrance, G.W., O'Brien, B.J. & Stoddart, G.L., 2015, *Methods for the Economic Evaluation of Health Care Programmes*, 4th edn, New York, NY: Oxford University Press

Muennig, P., 2002, *Designing and Conducting Cost-Effectiveness Analyses in Medicine and Health Care*, San Francisco, CA: Jossey-Bass

5

The project planning phase: what will you do, and how?

Chapter outline

Why plan at all?
The project charter
    Strategies: how the objectives will be achieved
    Project scope
    Defining deliverables
    Project governance
    Identifying and engaging stakeholders
    Finalising the project charter
The project plan
Planning for project assurance
Project structures
    Functional structures
    The matrix system
Planning for human resource needs
Risk management
Issue management
The quality plan

Communications planning
Managing project change
Organisational change management planning
Planning project logistics
The project information system
Planning for evaluation
Tips for conducting project planning
Summary
Readings and resources

Taking the time to properly plan a project can make the difference between project success and a troubled project that fails to deliver. Planning is the method by which the team works out how to make the project happen. A project plan addresses the 'what, who, how, when and at what cost'. It makes a project team more effective in achieving its aims and more capable of acquiring and using the right resources and methods. Good planning means selecting achievable aims and objectives, designing feasible means, managing the workload, identifying risks and issues, making the best use of everyone's talents and establishing the basis for good decision-making. Almost all project management literature stresses that good project design and planning are critical to project success. The project plan is the blueprint for the entire project, and is the guide for all project activities. Planning for evaluation of the project is also a key activity in the planning phase (see Chapter 6).

In this chapter, we give a step-by-step outline for writing a good project plan and identify the issues that need to be resolved at this stage. In Chapter 7, we deal with some important technical planning methods— scheduling, budgeting and preparing a business case. These techniques can be critical for larger and more complex projects (although we note that all projects require a schedule, and a budget of some kind).

Why plan at all?

> Failing to plan is planning to fail.
>
> *(Attributed to Winston Churchill)*

Despite the good sense and obvious benefits of planning, there is often strong resistance to undertaking formal or detailed project planning.

There can be pressure to get a project done quickly, and it can be very tempting to get on with the actual work of the project as soon as possible, and either avoid planning or pay it lip service only.

There are many reasons for resistance to planning, and they include the following:

- Planning can be difficult (it forces people to think—it requires negotiation, collaboration, consensus and decision-making).
- Many people believe that plans are a waste of time because inevitably plans change during the course of a project.
- For most people, planning is not as satisfying as actually doing the work and hopefully getting quick results.
- People lack the skills for planning.
- A project plan can be seen as too bureaucratic rather than as a working tool.
- Rational planning to determine the implementation or go-live date may conflict with the desire to 'name the date' that the team must work to.

Failure to start with a clear plan almost guarantees that your project will not be successful, because there will not be sufficient definition of what you are going to do or how you are going to do it. Without a project plan (addressing 'what, who, how, when and at what cost'), and without the plan being agreed to or signed off, it is likely that there will be general confusion, lack of common understanding and higher costs; the likelihood of project success is diminished. Of course, the size and nature of the project will determine how elaborate the plan needs to be, and how much time and energy will be needed to prepare it.

It needs to be recognised that the time taken for planning and development can be anywhere up to a third of the total project timeframe and can equal the time spent on project implementation.

Senior managers are often tempted to 'name the date' when the project will be completed or will go-live, and will expect the project to be retrofitted to that timeline. In some instances there are imperative business drivers, such as the opening of a building or commencement of a clinical service. But often the date chosen is more arbitrary—for example, the end of the financial year, or a visit by a politician or dignitary for a 'turning of the sod' photo opportunity. Unrealistic timeframes that are not based on a good understanding of the scope, tasks and resources will jeopardise the feasibility of the project. Compromise, or finding the middle ground, can be the answer in these situations, where the project manager will need to understand the logic and assumptions of the decision-makers, as well as inform them about aspects of the project that would need to be adjusted (such as scope, resources or procurement) to meet the required timeline. Sometimes, careful planning processes can solve these problems, as Case 5.1 illustrates.

The quality of the planning effort can also be crucial in the successful delivery of a project. In particular, a key cause of failure of ICT-enabled projects can be directly linked to the adequacy of project planning, as was the finding of the Victorian Ombudsman's investigation of ICT-enabled projects in the Victorian public health system (Victorian Ombudsman 2011, p. 70).

Before we work through the planning processes and activities, we need to recognise that many newcomers to planning are sceptical about it, precisely because of the rational basis behind it. Working life is hardly ever as logical as the plan—people act in ways that are not imagined in rationales, goals and strategies, and may well set out to deliberately undermine or sabotage projects.

Sometimes circumstances mean that a project cannot 'start at the beginning', or that the rationale for the project has to be assembled after other decisions have already been made, or that the timeline is patently not achievable. Sometimes circumstances change during the life of the project. Sometimes the project team makes promises to stakeholders that it cannot keep, or the executive has another good idea that changes the project scope.

The value of planning can seem doubtful for **soft projects** (defined as complex undertakings aimed at intangible results). Most organisational change and service development projects have at least some of the characteristics of soft projects. That is (compared to building projects, for example), the objectives and scope are more likely to change after commencement, costs are more difficult to estimate and the logical relationships between activities are not as concrete (McElroy 1996, p. 327). However, experience with such projects (arguably the majority in the health and community services sector) indicates that planning is especially valuable in conditions of uncertainty.

It is also important to remember that, like the project life cycle (see Chapter 3), planning is often an iterative process. The project may start with a clear plan, but the objectives might change when strategies are

Case 5.1 Naming the date versus planning and scheduling

The executive of a health service had just signed off an agreement with a web development company to develop a new public website for the organisation. It was announced to staff that the new website would be launched on 1 July, at the start of the new financial year (because the funding for the project needed to be spent by 30 June, the end of the financial year). But it was 1 April, and the project manager had just been assigned the brief. A quick planning process involving the web developer, project team, project sponsor and key stakeholders identified the following schedule estimates:

- initiation—establishment of project team, planning, steering committee (2 weeks)
- design—review and approval of site map, look and feel and functions (5 weeks)
- content gathering and update—gathering website content and review (6 weeks)
- review and sign-off of new website design and content (3 weeks)
- website programming by the vendor (6 weeks)
- testing, review and launch (2 weeks).

By setting tight timelines and taking opportunities for activities to occur in parallel, the project manager determined that the project would take 20 weeks, with a launch date of 20 August. The project manager consulted finance staff, and devised a payment schedule with incentives for early completion of 'billable' work so that all expenses could be reconciled to 30 June. In this case, the project manager was successful in convincing the executive (partly because the logic of the plan was so clear), and it was agreed that the website would be launched in August.

better developed in the early stages of implementation. New possibilities might open up, or anticipated resources might shrink. There can be frequent movement between planning and implementing activities, particularly at the beginning of a project. Detailed planning for activities within the implementation phase—for example, testing, training and go-live—may often be done just prior to the activity commencing.

Table 5.1 identifies the common processes and activities of planning. Not all the activities may be required for every project, and similarly, additional components such as procurement, project assurance and contingency plans may be required for some projects. Please note that some of the processes mentioned below are explained fully in Chapter 7.

The key point is that hardly anything goes exactly according to plan, but having a plan helps you to deal with the challenges of real life

Table 5.1 Project planning process and activities

Components of the project plan	Activities
Project charter	Defining the goals, objectives and strategies
Scope and deliverables	Defining how big the project is going to be, what is within or outside its boundaries, and specifying what the project will produce
Project structures, governance and stakeholders	• Identifying the project sponsor and stakeholders • Locating the project in the organisation structure • Designing project committees and decision-making processes • Determining how to involve consumers and other stakeholders
Activity definition, sequencing and timing (see Chapter 7)	• Development of the work breakdown structure (WBS); that is, the project tasks and activities, and the relationships between the activities • Estimation of how long each task will take
Schedule development (see Chapter 7)	Plotting project tasks against a timeline including project phases and decision points, deadlines, milestones and critical pathways
Human resources (see Chapter 7)	• Identifying the human resources required for the project • Building the project team
Resources, cost estimating and budgeting (see Chapter 7)	Defining and estimating the cost of the resources required for the project, and development of the project budget

Components of the project plan	Activities
Risk and issue management	• Identifying what could go wrong (the risks), and the likelihood of it happening • Planning for contingencies and a process for resolving them • Planning for how project issues will be identified, documented and addressed
Project quality plan	Defining the quality standards to be met by the project outcomes and the systems for monitoring quality
Communication plan	Developing a project communication plan for informing stakeholders and reporting progress
Management of project change	Establishing change control and variation processes
Organisational change management plan	• Identifying the change impact of the project outside and beyond itself, including the staff and processes that will be impacted • Developing a plan for how the change impact will be managed
Evaluation planning (Chapter 6)	Identifying how the project is going to be evaluated, what tools will be used, what data are required and how they will be collected
Operational planning	Establishment of the project tools and information systems

Source: Adapted from PMI 2017.

and still get there in the end. Not having a plan is like negotiating the freeways of an unknown city without a map. You might be able to see the landmark you are headed for, but you are likely to end up somewhere completely different if you don't know the route.

The project charter

The project charter (also known as 'project definition' or **project initiation document [PID]**) is the first key element and foundation of the project plan. If a project proposal has been prepared (see Chapter 4), it will provide the basis for the project charter. Essentially the charter could be described as the rules of the game by which the project runs. Everything else in the plan is based on achieving the project as defined in the project charter. Getting the charter right is often the vital first step in planning, and this is where critical thinking about the project is concentrated and the project design is fundamentally set. When projects or a subset of tasks are undertaken by external consultants, the project charter will be a key part of the contract.

The key steps in preparing the project charter are:
- confirming/developing the goals and objectives (see Chapter 4)
- outlining strategies and approaches
- defining the scope (that is, the limits)
- defining deliverables
- identifying key stakeholders.

Strategies: how the objectives will be achieved

The simplest way to think about the strategies for a project is to consider each objective and ask: How will it be achieved? What needs to be done?

Some questions follow that may be useful when identifying the need for particular strategies:
- Is this effectively an initial development and trial, and, if so, how will it inform broader implementation?
- Is there a need for the approach to be piloted, the methods proven or the feasibility assessed?
- Will the project be staged or rolled out over time, or have a single implementation phase?
- For a staged implementation, which groups/areas would start first and what is the remaining order?
- What standards, policies or guidelines will be applied to the project?
- What approach will be used to engage key stakeholders/groups?
- What training and change management methods will be used?

The project charter should describe the strategies in enough detail for the project team, stakeholders and decision-makers to understand how the project will achieve its goals and objectives. Small, simple projects may not always need all three levels of goals, objectives and strategies. However, among these three levels it is the objectives that can occasionally be skipped, never the goals or strategies.

Project scope

Defining and sticking to the project scope is one of the cornerstones of good project management, as the scope statement puts some boundaries on the project (Verzuh 2012). Both failure to define and control the scope and 'scope creep' (unmanaged changes to scope—usually expansion) can be major factors in projects failing to meet timelines and budgets, or in outright failure. According to Hayes & Miller (2002), only one in five of all major projects actually meets schedule and budgetary goals. Many of the reasons for failure to meet the money and time objectives are found in the way the project was designed and how the boundaries around it were drawn.

Clarifying scope by having a scope statement in the project charter is the best way to safeguard the project. A scope statement should describe the major activities of the project and their limits in such a way that it will be absolutely clear if extra work is added later on (Verzuh 2012). Often this is achieved by specifying what the project will *not* do (project **exclusions**), as these examples show:

- 'The system will be implemented in all Aurora Health campuses and locations, but excludes co-located services such as Rolling Valley Community Health and Eastern Dialysis services.'
- 'Training will be developed and delivered to all ICU staff but will not include ongoing eLearning modules being delivered as part of the continuing professional development program.'
- 'The project scope includes the piloting and evaluation of the new medication protocol, but not its implementation.'

The scope statement can also define where the project sits in relation to a larger or related project.

Defining deliverables

The deliverables are simply the answer to the question 'what will this project deliver?' They will mostly include a report and, depending on the project, perhaps a piece of software, a process improvement, a new job design, a training package or any other product commissioned as part of the project. Consulting contracts often include a detailed statement of the products or outputs of the project that will be handed over to the client at the end of the contract. This concept can also be useful for internal projects, by forcing a clear delineation of the product or output in more concrete terms than the goals or objectives.

Project governance

The project charter normally also includes a section outlining the proposed approach to project governance and decision-making, and the important task of engaging stakeholders.

The steering committee

Steering committees, advisory committees and reference groups can help to make or break projects. The term 'steering committee' (also known as 'project board' in PRINCE2® or sometimes called a 'project control group') usually implies some level of control and ownership over the project, indicating that the committee's decisions will literally steer the project in the direction the committee wishes it to go. Reference groups and advisory committees usually play a less hands-on role, providing advice and support, and helping the project to work well. The design of the project committee, and its way of working, will depend partly on whether the project is internally focused (for example, the reorganisation of care processes) or externally focused (for example, the development of an area health plan).

There are a number of critical issues in establishing the project management structure (Axelos 2017):

- clarifying the role and decision-making capacities of the project committee
- gaining appropriate representation on the committee
- giving the committee authority to make decisions and commit resources to the project
- identifying an effective chairperson who can facilitate interactive meetings
- motivating members to persist with an often complex and demanding process
- dealing with questions of confidentiality or conflicts of interest
- ensuring community participation if relevant
- securing participation by other parts of the organisation.

In the PRINCE2® approach, an empowered steering committee is chaired by the project sponsor (or executive in charge of the project). The committee takes responsibility for signing off the various stages of the project and its final outcome. It makes decisions that are needed at this level all along the way, and acts as a sounding board for the project manager and team.

The committee is made up of senior representatives of the major stakeholder groups—that is, those who will use or work with the results of the project (the 'users'), and those who are required to deliver services or capacity to support the project outcomes (the 'suppliers'). A deliberate role distinction is made: the suppliers are asked to monitor costs and feasibility, while the users are asked to focus on functionality and quality. For example, in a project that aims to introduce a new information system into an emergency department, the IT department of the hospital will have a strong interest, along with emergency clinicians (medical and nursing), the health information and clerical staff of the department, and staff who manage the flow of patients into receiving wards. Representatives of the IT department and some administrative staff would be asked to take the role of suppliers on the committee, and their vested interest in having a system that is efficient, and easy to maintain and support, is then formally recognised. Representatives of the clinicians, bed managers and other administrative staff are asked to take the role of users, and their interest in ease of use and quality of data is thus recognised. The health information staff (who manage medical records) might need to have a seat at both ends of this table.

In the PRINCE2® approach (Axelos 2017, p. 62), the duties of the steering committee or project board are to:

- be accountable for the project
- provide unified direction
- delegate effectively
- facilitate cross-functional integration
- commit resources
- ensure effective decision-making
- support the project manager
- ensure effective communication.

We suggest that the terms of reference of the committee are best outlined in the project charter, and refined and finalised in the early stages of implementation. Any potentially difficult issues should be dealt with up-front in a businesslike way to prevent them from becoming really difficult and heated issues further down the track.

The role of the project sponsor

The sponsor or champion is somebody senior in the organisation who authorises the project and usually fulfils most or all of the following functions:

- chairing the project steering committee or working group
- acting as the supervisor of the project manager
- ensuring that the project team has good access to people and resources across the organisation, as needed by the project

- keeping the executive informed of progress, and ensuring their continued support
- signing off (sometimes on behalf of the committee) on major decisions or variations as part of the project, and receiving the final report.

The sponsor may have been identified in the initiation phase of the project, and been actively engaged with the tasks of defining the role and responsibilities for incorporation into the plan. If the project is contracted out, the equivalent role is generally played by the person who is 'the client' (who may be the person who signs the contract), and the functions are similar.

Identifying and engaging stakeholders

Stakeholders are the individuals and organisations who are actively involved in the project, or whose interests may be affected as a result of the project, or who may exert influence over the project and its results (PMI 2017, p. 503). In the planning phase, the project team needs to identify the stakeholders, plan for their engagement and identify their interests and allegiances, which can affect the project. While this identification is not always easy, most projects will have stakeholders who fall into the following categories:

- Sponsor or champion—person or group who provides the finances as well as executive management support for the project.
- Customers or users—the people, groups or organisations that use or consume the project's product or outcomes.
- Partners and allies—the organisations and individuals whose contributions or support is needed.
- Performing organisation or department—the organisation or department whose employees are most directly involved in doing the work.
- Sometimes the project personnel themselves are also considered as stakeholders:
  - Project manager—the person nominated to manage the project.
  - Project team members—the group performing the work of the project.

Once stakeholders have been identified, it is useful to consider the impact that a particular stakeholder group may have on the project, and how they will be managed. Stakeholders may have the power to veto or approve, delay, facilitate, derail or guide a project. Stakeholder management in internal projects has its own challenges—for example, there is often no defined 'client' to accept or reject outcomes. Individuals may have roles in both supplying inputs to the project and using its outputs, and the interests of stakeholders are sometimes seen as a kind of zero sum game—that is, one person's win is another's loss. In these circumstances, stakeholder paralysis is a real threat to projects that seek to change the way business is done.

A simple map of the stakeholders is a useful planning tool that can help with preparation for active management of stakeholders' issues in the implementation phase, as represented in Table 5.2.

To complete the mapping exercise, stakeholders are identified and categorised as to whether they are supportive of or opposed to the project, and rated for their relative importance—that is, the amount of power or influence they can exert on the project. Strategies for managing the way stakeholders engage with the project can then be developed, with the aim of minimising opposition and maximising support.

Involving consumers

Consumers, patients or clients as a stakeholder group need to be considered—consumer engagement can add value in several ways. The following factors are relevant to this decision:

- Will the project have a direct impact on care or services for patients/clients?
- Will the rights of consumers (for example, to privacy, or self-determination) be affected by the project?
- Are there issues of equity of access and appropriateness of service for population groups with special needs (for example, people with disabilities or mental illness, Aboriginal people or recent immigrants)?
- Are there established advocacy or interest groups who can offer expertise and who might affect (positively or negatively) the success of the project?

The next question is to determine how consumers can be involved. While representation (for example, on steering or advisory committees) is one method, it isn't necessarily the best way. Focus groups, surveys and consultative groups (focused on the consumer perspectives and priorities) can make better use of consumers' limited time and energy.

Table 5.2 Stakeholder mapping

	Not important	Very important
Hinder	Problematic—need to be monitored	Antagonistic—need active strategies for management
Support	Low priority—keep on side	Champions—work with them

Finalising the project charter

For many projects, the charter will also refer to the expected timeline and the overall budget requirements, but these aspects tend to be fully defined as part of development of the full plan. With the goals, objectives, strategies, scope, deliverables and key stakeholders defined, the project charter is now complete and can undergo a review and approval process. The approved project charter can be published to all who are associated with the project and then used as the basis for establishing the project and demonstrating management support for the project and the project manager (Verzuh 2012).

The project plan

With the project charter developed and agreed, the remaining planning effort is directed at working out and documenting all the major resources and methods required to give life to the project. The length and complexity of the plan is primarily dependent on the size and scope of the project. Some organisations have templates and defined processes for the development of the project plan, and may stipulate what should be included in the document. Completed project plans can vary from about five pages to about fifty (or even more for large and complex projects).

The more carefully the plan is thought through, the more likely it is that the project will stay on track and the fewer surprises (or crises) there will be in the implementation and closing phases. Energy spent in developing the plan to a sufficient level of detail, in collaboration with stakeholders, will result in greater understanding by all of what is expected of them as part of the project. In this way, much potential conflict can be avoided, or at least be identified and made more manageable.

The remaining planning effort and contents of the project plan address the following elements:
- project assurance
- project structures
- activity definition, sequencing and timing (see Chapter 7)
- schedule development (see Chapter 7)
- human resources
- project resources (see Chapter 7)
- risk and issue management
- quality
- communication
- management of project change
- organisational change management
- project logistics
- evaluation (See Chapter 6).

If the project is a small one, some of these headings might need only half a page in the project plan, but even small projects benefit from attention to each component. It is also important for the project plan to include any assumptions and dependencies that must be met before the project commences, or that may affect how and when it will progress. For example, it may be assumed that a government policy will be introduced by a certain date, or a project 'go-live' date may be dependent on a building redevelopment being on time.

The next area of planning—identifying the activities and tasks of the project—gets to the core of the work program, and the resources that will be needed to achieve it.

Planning for project assurance

To heed the lessons of past health project failures, and in recognition of significant investment, many government-funded projects are increasingly subject to intense scrutiny via independent audit, **gateway reviews** and **project assurance** requirements. Aimed at minimising the risk of project failure and enabling effective oversight of progress and outcomes, project assurance practices are increasingly common practice, and need to be identified during the planning phase. Project or program assurance is a discipline that seeks to provide independent and objective oversight of the likely future performance of major projects for those responsible for sanctioning, financing or insuring such undertakings (Wikipedia 2018b).

The Gateway Review Process is a project assurance methodology developed in the United Kingdom to improve the delivery of major projects. It involves short, sharp and confidential reviews conducted by reviewers not associated with the project at six key stages of the project life cycle, also known as 'gates' (Australian National Audit Office 2012).

The following is a list of common project assurance requirements that may need to be planned for (adapted from Victoria State Government, Department of Treasury and Finance 2018):

- external/government representation on the project steering and governance bodies
- external/independent review of the business case
- independent audit of the project budget (and sometimes independent costings) and risk/mitigation plan
- regular performance reporting
- project assurance reviews
- gateway reviews—audit, reviews, actioning of review reports, reporting.

Project structures

Planning for the location of the project within the organisational structure, and specifying its reporting lines and access to decision-makers, can prevent unhelpful project politics later on. The project manager's role will likewise be made easier if their place in the structure and the decision-making systems is clear and appropriate to the task. The question of structure is more straightforward for external projects, where the team sits entirely (or mostly) outside the organisation. For internal projects, there are several structural options in common use, and no one right model.

Functional structures

Functional structures (where the project is 'owned' by the unit or department most involved, the usual employer of most of the project team) have several advantages. They tend to have maximum flexibility in the use of their staff; individual experts can be utilised for many different projects; and specialists can be grouped to share knowledge and experience. However, a number of problems can also arise in this kind of structure. The project may suffer from a lack of focus and attention when it is competing with ongoing tasks, and the management of the unit may not be well placed to cope with project characteristics such as more urgent timelines. The project may require the unit to work with other parts of the organisation or another service provider in a way that is at odds with its ongoing relationships.

When projects within a functional unit come unstuck, the typical outcome is that they slip down the priority list and are delayed, down-graded or allowed to fade away.

The best predictors of success in this structure are that:
• the project is championed by the unit manager
• the team has authority to make decisions about the project
• the project deals with an issue that matters to the staff in their daily work.

The matrix system

The main alternative structure is the matrix system, where project staff are drawn from functional units, thus cutting across the organisation structure for the life of the project. The project manager reports to an executive or senior manager in the role of project sponsor, and the team members report to the project manager, at least for the purposes of the project. The advantages of a matrix structure are that projects and project teams are given a strong identity within the organisation, and resources are allocated accordingly. The downsides can include conflicts between line managers and project staff, undermining of the traditional organisation, conflict for staff who work part-time on the project between their ongoing and project roles, and unclear roles and responsibilities (Alsène 1999, p. 367). Case 5.2 illustrates the problem.

Case 5.2 Conflict between projects and operations

A health service established a project to implement national hospital emergency access targets within the organisation. The project manager tasked with planning and implementing the new access plan came from the quality and safety unit, while the project team was made up of representatives from the access management group, emergency department (ED) (medical and nursing), the heads of the surgical and medical units, the redesigning care team, IT and health information departments.

The project was sponsored by the executive director of nursing, and was given high priority, with an implementation period of four months. A matrix structure emerged by default rather than planning, with team members reporting to both their line manager and the project manager.

Great progress was made until the project required more time from the clinical staff than was anticipated (partly because of the short timeline). Releasing staff from shifts in the ED became increasingly difficult for the nurse unit manager, because of the needs of the daily operations of the department and the pressure on inpatient beds. In particular, the ED staff were caught between their daily responsibilities in the unit (some were accused of 'skiving off' and letting the team down) and effective participation in the project. There was also a common perception among ED staff that the project goal (to achieve compliance with four-hour ED admission targets for patients awaiting a ward bed) was purely a political target that was at odds with good patient care.

It became clear to the project manager and the executive that if the project was to stay on track, the resource costs to replace ('backfill') clinician staff time on the project would need to be covered. The project benefits to the ED staff and the organisation also needed to be better understood. It was time to revisit the plan, the budget and the stakeholder engagement strategy.

Planning for human resource needs

People make projects happen.

(Verzuh 2012)

Working out the human resource requirements and how to build the project team are critical tasks for many projects, and some steps can be taken at the planning stage, based on the project charter, WBS and timelines. Often writing the detailed project plan is the first task of the newly appointed project manager, so some of the key questions below may have already been answered:

- What kind of skills are needed to achieve this project?
- Are these skills available within the organisation or will they need to be sourced from outside?
- Which of those skills are needed by the manager?
- What other people with particular skills are needed, how much of their time and how many of them?
- How will technical or specialist expertise not available among team members be brought in?
- What processes will be used for selecting the project manager and other team members?
- Who will the project manager report to?
- How much authority over team members will the manager have?

This is the time when organisations that have nurtured project capability and skills within the organisation (or have more project experience or an established Project Management Office) will be seeing the benefits of their investment. On the other hand, contracting for project management and team members may be a necessary or desirable strategy.

Because of the uniqueness of each project, it is rare for an organisation to have all the necessary skills in-house for a major project. So consultants and temporary specialist staff are often engaged either to work directly on a project or to backfill operational positions. The nature of the relationship between contracted staff and the project manager and/or sponsor needs to be well planned and communicated. During the planning phase, it may be useful to draft position descriptions for the project team members, which enables a quick start to the recruitment process if required.

Consultants can add real value to a project by bringing high-order skills, up-to-date knowledge, the objectivity of an outsider and a greater freedom to deliver uncomfortable messages or challenge the prevailing culture. On the negative side, working with consultants and contractors can be a knowledge drain for the organisation and may also require additional resources to manage the contract. Contracts can include a requirement for the consultants to transfer knowledge and skills, and to hand over all the 'intelligence' gathered as part of the project (in the form of briefings as well as organised files). This can help the organisation get value for money from the consultancy and will reduce the likelihood of future dependency on a particular consultant or firm.

Risk management

Risk management is the means by which uncertainty is systematically managed to increase the likelihood of meeting project objectives (Verzuh 2012). Risk management is essentially designed to answer three questions: What might go wrong? How will it be handled? What can we do to prevent it, or reduce its likelihood? The related task of managing problems, opportunities and errors that arise during the project is generally known as 'issue management'.

All projects encounter uncertainty, and there is always the risk that something will happen to jeopardise the budget, the quality, the timelines, the stakeholder support and, ultimately, the achievement of the project's aims and its sustainability. Good planning includes a process for identifying project risks, understanding their potential severity and planning ways to respond if the risk becomes reality.

The aim of risk management is to control and reduce risk. The first step is to analyse the project to identify the sources of risk. This is perhaps best achieved by starting with consultation or a meeting with stakeholders to ask the critical questions, and then creating a risk management plan. What can happen to cause problems for this project? Will there be enough staff to cover the roster? Will the new equipment be delivered on time? Will industrial activity impact on the timeline? Will the software pass testing? Will there be a change of government policy or corporate leadership?

After defining the possible risks, including their potential impact on the project (that is, what is the result if the risk turns into reality?), each risk can be assigned a probability rating. Then a strategy (also called a **contingency**) can be developed to respond to the risks and reduce possible damage to the project and the organisation. To manage project risk effectively, a risk management plan should be developed as part of the planning process. This plan then provides the basis for the project risk register during implementation. Table 5.3 illustrates one component of a risk management plan for the project of conducting a community survey.

Project risks are classified according to the likelihood of their occurring and the seriousness of the consequences or impact if they do occur. The likelihood may range from rare (for example, the chances of an earthquake) to almost certain (for example, the chances of minor

Table 5.3 Risk management for community survey project

Information	Description	Example
Risk	Description of the risk	Not enough community members are willing to complete the questionnaire
Risk impact	What is the impact of the risk on the organisation and/or the project if the risk is realised?	Reliability of survey results is reduced
Likelihood	How likely is the risk to be realised (see risk matrix)	Likely
Consequence	What is the severity of the consequence if the risk is realised? (see risk matrix)	Moderate
Level of risk	The severity level of the realised risk when considering likelihood and consequence (see risk matrix)	Moderate
Contingencies	What strategies can be put in place to respond to the risk to reduce the impact?	Extend the survey timeline and continue recruitment. Gather information by alternate means, e.g. focus groups or interview.
Mitigation	How can the risk be minimised?	Involve community leaders and staff who are influential to promote community participation
Risk owner	Which person or party has the responsibility for managing the risk and putting contingencies in place?	Project manager
Date logged	When was the risk identified?	22 April
Date of review	When was the risk last reviewed?	15 October

vandalism in the car park), whereas the consequences may range from insignificant to catastrophic (for example, complete failure of the project or injury to patients). The risk level is assigned by plotting these two attributes of risk in the risk matrix (see Figure 5.1).

Figure 5.1 Risk matrix

Consequence / Likelihood	Insignificant	Minor	Moderate	Major	Catastrophic
Almost certain					
Likely					
Moderate					
Unlikely					
Rare					

Level of risk			
Low	Moderate	High	Extreme

Source: Adapted from PRINCE2® (Axelos 2017, p. 130)

Verzuh (2012) describes various approaches to the issue of reducing project risk:

- Accept the risk—that is, choose to do nothing about it.
- Avoid the risk—choose not to do part of the project.
- Monitor the risk—and prepare contingency plans.
- Transfer the risk—for example, by taking out insurance.
- Mitigate the risk—in other words, reduce the risk.

Once risks are understood, it is possible to identify contingencies—the 'what if' issues—and plan the response. Capital building and engineering projects always include a contingency allowance—that is, money set aside for unforeseen circumstances, traditionally about 10 per cent of the total cost. Projects in health and community services are often budgeted to the last penny, with no capacity for a contingency allowance. But even if adding an actual contingency allowance is not possible, there is usually a way to slip in some flexibility or some discretionary resources. If something goes wrong, resources allocated to another component of the project could perhaps be shifted without impacting on the core objectives; or some potential slack in the project timelines could be taken up; or the scope could be squeezed by cutting back on less important elements.

As part of contingency planning, it is important to plan for an escalation procedure. To '**escalate**' means taking the project issue higher in the organisation in order for it to be resolved, or implementing the next level of action required to overcome an identified risk.

Issue management

During the course of the project, problems, situations, opportunities, questions and errors can arise that are generally referred to as 'issues'. An issue can be defined as a problem or obstacle that the project team does not have the answer to or the power to resolve (Verzuh 2012). Examples of issues could be delay in the supply of a project resource, a policy conflict exposed by the project, a key stakeholder either leaving or joining the project, or any unforeseen situation not dealt with in the project plan. An issues log enables issues to be documented when they arise and thus provides the basis for assigning responsibility and ensuring the issue is addressed. It also establishes a record of how the issue was resolved or managed. The contents of a simple issues log are described in Table 5.4.

Table 5.4 Issues log

Issue ID	Unique identifier, usually a number, assigned as each issue is identified
Description	What is the issue, and what is the impact if it is not resolved?
Assigned to	The project team member (or project manager) responsible for pursuing resolution
Date identified	Date the issue was originally added to the log
Current status/ last action	The date of the last action, a description of the action, and the current status of the issue. Leave all the action/status lines in the log as a record of how the action was pursued. Keeping closed issues in the log is one form of project history.

The quality plan

Every project aims to reach a standard of quality in its outcome, at the least in order to be 'fit for purpose', and perhaps to meet external standards (for accreditation or other benchmarks) or to fit with the quality systems of the organisation. The project charter is again the source document for quality planning. What are the standards that each of the major deliverables or outcomes must meet? Are there process standards that apply (for example, 'consultation with unions is conducted in accordance with the organisation's formal agreements')? Who needs to be satisfied with the quality achieved?

Each project will have unique specifications, standards or criteria that need to be met. For example, a new information system for patient location search in a hospital might require an average response time of three seconds or less; a new strength and balance program for older people might have to achieve a high standard of safety. These requirements provide the elements for the project's quality plan. A simple quality plan for an emergency department project (introducing a new patient management system) is shown in Table 5.5.

Table 5.5 Quality plan for emergency department patient management system

Quality of outcomes	Measurement	Who assesses
• The flow of patients through the department is efficient and safe • The information needs of clinicians are met • Administrative staff can meet their workloads with current staffing levels	• Meets specifications for timelines and continuity of care • Meets specifications; no losses of information currently available • Workload of new systems is at worst equal to existing	• Directors (medical and nursing) of ED • Senior medical and nursing staff representatives • Administration manager
Process and indicators	Measurement	Who assesses
• Patient care is not disrupted during implementation • Staff are consulted and engaged in changes affecting them	• No adverse impact on patients is recorded during implementation • Meets organisational change agreement standards	• Directors of ED • Human resource consultant

Communications planning

Inevitably, almost all aspects of projects rely on effective communication—from policy decisions to meeting times. A breakdown in communication can be a project showstopper and is worth spending time on in the planning phase.

A communication plan is the written strategy for getting the right information to the right people at the right time (Verzuh 2012). All the project stakeholders will need information on a more or less regular basis, so even a simple plan outlining who requires the information, what information they need and when they need it, is useful. A simple communication plan might look like the one outlined in Table 5.6.

Table 5.6 A simple communication plan

Stakeholder	Information required	Frequency	Medium
Sponsor	High-level cost, quality, problems and proposed solutions	Monthly	Written report and meeting
Sponsor	Risk escalation	As necessary	Phone, email
Project team	Detailed schedule, problems, news, coordination information	Weekly	Meeting and status report
All interested parties	Occasional news of the project	As and when required	e-newsletter

As part of a communication plan, a standard format for reporting progress to stakeholders will help enable rapid and consistent communication. Template 5.1 for a project **status report** (including communication plan reporting) is provided at the back of the book. It is also useful to think about how other reports and communication can be as timely as possible, whether through flyers, regular meetings, newsletters, email updates, intranet notice boards, message boards and/or blogs. A major project might employ non-formal communication strategies, as illustrated by Case 5.3. A useful principle when planning communications is to err on the side of more rather than less, as it is difficult to overcommunicate.

Managing project change

Projects never unfold exactly as planned, no matter how good the planning has been, and variations (or **variances**) are a normal part of project implementation. At the planning stage, it is important to anticipate the need for variations and design a process for identifying, documenting and managing project change. This is called project change

Case 5.3 The Friday Facts

The project manager for a multisite project published a one- to two-page update on the project's intranet site every Friday for 52 weeks—inevitably known as 'The Friday Facts'. All interested people in five collaborating organisations spread over several states received an email notification when it was uploaded. The information was factual, the language informal and it looked good. Staff across the five sites appreciated being included and informed of the 'big picture'. For them, it was an easy way to keep up with the project, and it also contributed to overcoming the barriers of distance in this complex project.

management, as distinct from organisational change management (see the next section).

There are a number of formal tools for managing project change, and they can be adapted to suit the needs of the project and the style of the organisation. PRINCE2® and other frameworks call for a register or log of changes and a process to formally request changes to such aspects of the project as scope, timelines and deliverables. Such a register records the following for each change: the problem/change title, originator, date notified, project manager approval date, sponsor/client/steering committee approval date, implementation notes and, if relevant, change to the project completion date.

Organisational change management planning

The challenge at the beginning of a project and in the planning phase is to imagine what the organisational impact of the project will be, so that it can be effectively planned for and managed.

There are many change management planning resources available on the internet, including frameworks, processes and templates. The following list describes eight elements of an effective change management process (Smartsheet 2018), of which steps 1 to 3 would be performed in the initiation and planning phases:

1. Identify what will be improved—improvements may be a process, product, benefit or an outcome.

2. Present a solid business case to stakeholders—see Chapter 7.
3. Plan for the change—develop a change management plan.
4. Provide resources and use data for evaluation—resources can include people, equipment, software and tools (for example training tools).
5. Communication—the 'golden thread' that runs throughout the entire practice of change management, and contained in a communication plan.
6. Monitor and manage resistance—identify the roadblocks and resistance to change.
7. Celebrate success—recognise the success of teams and individuals involved.
8. Review, revise and continuously improve—change is an ongoing process, and change management strategies are commonly adjusted.

It is noted that many of the elements of effective change management described above overlap with other project initiation, planning and implementation activities. (See Chapter 8.)

The change impact of a project may be significant for specific individuals, for a particular role and for the organisation as a whole. During the planning phase, the focus is on anticipating the impact of change, or how it is going to be identified later, so that it can be managed effectively. For projects that entail significant change in the way services are delivered, or the way business processes are conducted (for example, introducing an electronic medical record [EMR]), it may be necessary to map the existing processes and the points of change during the planning stage in order to identify the change impact of the project.

'Process mapping' (or 'business process review') involves mapping workflows and information flows, sometimes using flow-charting software such as 'Visio™', to document current state and future processes. For example, when implementing a telemedicine service, a number of workflows (processes) for the doctor, nurse, allied health and administrative staff may be affected, including booking of the appointment, scheduling of the clinician time, documenting the consultation and billing.

It may not be necessary to conduct a full business process review in the planning phase, but simple high-level workflow mapping can assist in identifying aspects of the impact of change. These include who will be affected, and whether their role or responsibilities will change, as well as the location of their work and how they will carry out a process. For example, in the introduction of electronic pathology test ordering, major change in the workflow for clerical and courier staff is likely. Workflow mapping will also indicate current versus future state—what is changing, what is staying the same and what will no longer be done—and the team can then quantify the magnitude of change, what decisions will need to be made, and what policies will need to be reviewed and updated.

The project plan should include the strategies that you will use for identifying, quantifying and managing the organisational impact of the project, including change impact statements, business process review, stakeholder assessment, change readiness assessment and policy review, as well as communication and training.

Planning project logistics

The project will need some systems for its own operation, and some physical resources. The project plan should address the establishment processes and the required equipment, including information systems.

The following checklist highlights key issues:

- Is the project visible and identifiable—does it have a name or logo?
- Should the project be officially launched?
- Does the project have a home?
- Is there adequate space allocated for project team meetings, for workspace for project staff and for storage of project documents?
- Do you have the necessary resources, such as computers/mobile devices, access to photocopiers, telephones and stationery?
- Is the project manager known and identified as being the project manager?
- Is the project manager the main or the only contact, and do people know how to make contact with the project?
- Is there an agreed process or expectations for formation of the project team? Will staff be identified and asked to join the project or will they be seconded or recruited externally? (Be aware of the lead time to form the team—it can sometimes take months for staff to be released and become available to work on the project.)

The project information system

A vast array of information can be generated during the life of a project. The documentation and data might include both hard and soft copies of the project plan, training program, variation requests, progress and status reports, budget papers, scope documents, meeting minutes and agendas, WBS, Gantt and PERT charts or schedules, contracts, policies, discussion papers, invoices and purchase orders, correspondence and workshop reports.

Regardless of the size of your project, the plan should include a system for dealing with the data generated by it and with the information needed to manage it effectively. You may need to set up shared file directories that can be accessed by all the project stakeholders and team. Early planning can also enable the learnings from the project to be held and shared more effectively across the organisation, and contribute to future project success.

Planning for evaluation

Because each project offers a unique opportunity for learning from experience, evaluation is always of potential benefit. Evaluation needs to be planned for and built into the project at the planning stage, even for small projects—that is, the evaluation needs to be planned in advance, and starts while the project is actually running.

Evaluation approaches and methods are described in detail in Chapter 6.

Tips for conducting project planning

There are no magic solutions for overcoming the difficulties of project planning and estimation. But some things can help:

- seeking advice from colleagues with relevant expertise
- consulting management and stakeholders early to ensure support and shared understandings of limitations and constraints
- identifying the most effective planning methods and approaches for the project at hand
- learning from the experience of other projects—many evaluation reports and case studies are available both online and inside organisations
- committing yourself to targeted training

- contracting professional project planners or consultants to provide support and advice.

We noted at the beginning of this chapter that reality hardly ever works out in the precise, rational way that planning methods seem designed to achieve. This is not an argument against making a logical, detailed plan, but it does point to the need for skilled management and flexibility. Expecting the unexpected is the only possible outlook for project managers. In the next chapters we move to project management in action, and discuss how project teams manage what happens when the plan meets reality.

Summary

- Project planning is the critical success factor for projects, and the project plan is the central pillar of project management.
- The rational planning approach involves the development of achievable aims, objectives and strategies in a logical order, even though reality hardly ever works that way.
- Planning methods depend on the type and nature of the project, and many specialised methods for particular types and sizes of projects are available.
- The foundation of the project plan is the project charter, which defines scope and strategies as well as aims and objectives.
- The other elements of the project plan detail how the project charter will be implemented. They include project structure, the work program and resources, planning for risk and quality, communication planning, change management (both project and organisational), project logistics and evaluation planning.
- Project governance—committees and other forums—determines decision-making processes, but can also be well designed for managing stakeholders and coordinating the advice and inputs the project needs.
- Risk and issue management planning involves identifying what might go wrong, what will happen to the project if it does, how likely it is to happen, what contingency allowances can be made, and what approach to take to deal with each major risk.
- The quality plan specifies the standards that the project's outcomes must meet, and how their achievement will be monitored.

- Project logistics include getting the project established (office, name, logo and so on), the information systems the project will need and the communication plan.
- Even after writing a great plan, expect the unexpected.

Readings and resources

Benefits realisation framework:
www.pmi.org/learning/thought-leadership/series/benefits-realization/benefits-realization-management-framework

Benefits realisation plan: http://services.nsw.gov.au/sites/default/files/Benefits%20Realisation%20Plan%202011_0.doc

Change management plan template:
www.iscm.com.au/pdf/change-management-plan.pdf

Project assurance plan template:
www.dtf.vic.gov.au/gateway-review-process/project-assurance-reviews

Project communications template:
www.projectmanagementdocs.com/templates/communications-management-plan.html

Project issues register template:
www.egovernment.tas.gov.au/project_management/supporting_resources/templates

Project management guidebook:
www.thoughtware.com.au/documents/method123-ebook.pdf

Project management tools:
www.mindtools.com/pages/main/newMN_PPM.htm

Project planning:
http://en.wikipedia.org/wiki/Project_planning

Risk management planning:
www.wikihow.com/Develop-a-Risk-Management-Plan

6

Planning for evaluation: assessing project performance

Chapter outline

What is evaluation, and why do it?
Types of evaluation
    Process evaluation
    Impact evaluation
    Questions for designing process and impact evaluation
    Outcome evaluation
Evaluation approaches and design
    Program logic model
    Benefits realisation
    Evaluation planning and the seven-step approach
    Economic evaluation
    Post-Implementation Review
    Collecting and using data
    External or internal evaluation
Evaluation in practice—challenges and learning
Summary
Reading and resources

This chapter explains why project evaluation needs to be included in the project plan. It describes types of evaluation, and explains ways of incorporating evaluation design into the project to guide data collection throughout the project life cycle, and enable early identification of warning signs. At the end of the chapter, strategies for ensuring evaluation success and making evaluation results relevant to future projects and project design are discussed.

What is evaluation, and why do it?

> Evaluation is the systematic collection of information about the activities, characteristics, and results of programs to make judgments about the program, improve or further develop program effectiveness inform decisions about future programming, and/or increase our understanding.
>
> *(Patton 2008, p. 38)*

Evaluation is a way of getting answers to the questions: did it work, and why/why not? It is increasingly used in the financially constrained health and community services environment, where evidence-based practice in decision-making, project design and policy development is important. This applies particularly to mega-projects (with multi-million dollar budgets) with government or corporate involvement, where there is likely to be intense scrutiny of project outcomes and value for money (Cousins et al. 2014). For projects of all sizes, the need for financial accountability is driving increasingly close oversight, including the requirement for **project assurance**, independent audit and **gateway** processes and often the need to demonstrate bankable benefits.

Evaluation is one of the ways to generate knowledge and evidence to guide the sector in better service, program and project design. It is also true that smaller, in-house projects have been less likely to be formally evaluated, although some organisations are taking advantage of easier, scalable evaluation methods. Barriers to better use of project evaluation include that relevant evidence and reports are not easily accessible (Gray & Wilkinson 2016), and some organisations lack expertise in project evaluation.

When projects are used to test new methods of care or approaches to population health and wellbeing, project evaluation can help in deciding whether to continue or discontinue a service or program, or modify the goals and objectives, or change strategies to achieve the desired outcomes. Strategically, evaluation can generate evidence to promote successful strategies and share learnings, and can be used to support the continuation of new approaches or services in ongoing operations within the organisation, or across the field more broadly.

Evaluation is also defined as 'a structured process that creates and synthesizes information intended to reduce the level of uncertainty for stakeholders about a program or policy' (McDavid & Hawthorn 2006, p. 3). It is used to judge the value or worth of something by observing, measuring and comparing against an established criterion or standard (Hawe, Degeling & Hall 1990). Project evaluation provides evidence to monitor whether a project is progressing to plan, to identify its strengths and weaknesses, and to assist in deciding whether to modify existing strategies and/or develop new approaches to improve the next project. Evaluation also provides information to support the continuation or extension of a project, and can be used in demonstrating accountability to funders and community members (SACHRU 2012).

Types of evaluation

Evaluation can be applied to the process of the project, its outputs, and/ or its results, and preferably all three, so that everyone with an interest can understand what was done, whether it worked, and at least some of the reasons why. Generally, there are three types of evaluation: process, impact and outcome. This way of thinking about evaluation is based on systems theory—the idea that what happens in organisations or teams can be seen as consisting of inputs (e.g. money, equipment, staff), processes (work that uses the inputs) and outputs (the results).

Process evaluation

Process evaluation focuses on how a project is done, the implementation of strategies, the effectiveness of methods and the skill of their execution, and the overall quality of the project activities and output—what is actually produced by the project (sometimes called the **deliverables**). It is undertaken while the project is in operation, and its results can be analysed and used during the project as well as at the end.

Project failure could be the result of poor project design, poor or incomplete project implementation, lack of support from key stakeholders or other problems that arose during the project. These are things that can be identified by process evaluation. Or more positively, a well–developed project plan includes milestones, standards and criteria for assessing how the project is going as it unfolds. Using process evaluation to give people real-time feedback on what is happening can enhance the project's chances of success.

Process evaluation is designed to answer the questions of what is done, when, by whom, to whom, and how well. Examples of questions that are usually included in process evaluation are:

- Is the project operating as intended?
- Were project activities accomplished, and how well? If not, why not?
- What is the quality of each of the key project components?
- Are the interests of stakeholders being addressed?
- Is the project staying within budget?
- Are the planned outputs being delivered (during the project)?

Other questions will be more specific to the project. For example, when a project is trialling a new program or service, process evaluation can aid in understanding the relationship between specific program elements and outcomes (Saunders et al. 2005, p. 134) and answer additional questions such as:

- How well has the project reached the target population?
- How have external factors influenced program delivery?

Process evaluation can be conducted on an ongoing basis or at specific points during the project. A general guide is:

- Soon after a project has begun—collect and document descriptive information on project characteristics that will not change, and baseline information.
- During implementation—collect data on progress against timelines and objectives (such as recruitment, stakeholder engagement, conduct of planned activities, quality of resources used in the project).
- At the end of the project—analyse and document achievement of activity targets (such as attendance at workshops or group fitness, take-up of a new method by staff) and quality of outputs.

Table 6.1 provides an example of process evaluation to be done in the closing phase of a surgical admissions pathway project, using a combination of data already available from the project records, and some collected for the purpose of evaluation *(shown in italics)*.

Table 6.1 Process evaluation of a surgical admissions pathway project

Goal: To introduce a surgical admissions pathway for urgent patients straight to the receiving ward, and to test both its capacity to reduce the overall length of stay for those patients and its impact on emergency department (ED) waiting times for all patients.		
Process	**Questions**	**Data source**
Pathway development	Were staff representatives satisfied with the pathway development process?	Notes of consultations and workshops with staff representatives during the project; *notes of meeting held by an independent manager or clinical leader with staff representatives for this purpose, using questions prepared by the project team*
Stakeholder management	Were staff representatives satisfied with the project overall?	
	Was the change managed well?	Minutes of team and steering committee meetings; papers or proposals prepared by the team for the steering committee or other audiences; *notes of discussion at final steering committee meeting*
	Were other departments (including the IT department) satisfied with the project process?	Minutes of meetings and other evidence of engagement with other departments; *notes of discussion held with representatives of information services, finance, bed managers and so on for this purpose*
Communication	Were stakeholders well informed about the project, its progress and the nature of changes?	Summary of all formal communication about the project with stakeholders; *notes of meetings held for evaluation purposes listed above*

Governance	Was leadership and decision-making for the project effective?	Minutes of steering committee meetings; summary of formal reports to the executive; *notes of discussion at steering committee and with executive held for this purpose; notes of other meetings held for the purpose of evaluation*
Close and handover	• Was the project closure adequate? • Was handover effective?	Summary of closure activities; notes of all questions fielded by members of the project team or the surgical division executive in the first 30 days after handover; *responses to a survey of surgical wards, ED and other departments involved in the operation*

Source: Adapted from work by Mr Jason Cloonan.

Impact evaluation

Impact evaluation measures the extent to which the project's objectives have been achieved. It focuses on the immediate results at the end of the project. Impact evaluation can also assess unforeseen and unanticipated outcomes, whether beneficial or detrimental.

Impact evaluation can be a simple procedure. At its most basic, the question is 'did we achieve the objectives of the project?'. For example, if the objectives of the project were to install a new system or process and allow it to work, the question is 'is it installed and does it work?'. For some projects, this may be all that is done, and all that the organisation needs. But the impact evaluation questions for larger or more complex projects require more thought, and the project manager may need to choose or design **evaluation indicators** to make the impact of complex changes measurable. For example, in assessing the impact of a new model of care that requires nurses to work differently, sick leave levels may be an excellent indicator of real acceptance of change, to complement data on the level of compliance with the new method.

A word about terms: readers may have encountered different usage of the terms **impact** and **outcome**. In Australia (but not in some other countries like the United States) 'impact' is used to denote the immediate results, and 'outcome' for the longer-term results. So, in public health interventions, the impact of an immunisation project would be measured in terms of the proportion of the target population who were immunised at the completion of the project, whereas the outcomes could not be measured until much later (i.e. fewer cases of vaccine-preventable diseases in the area). For a project that prepared an organisation for a change in funding arrangements, the impact would be measured by preparations being completed on time. Outcome could be measured as successful management of services and budget under the new funding rules, but that would come well after the project was completed.

Some other examples of impact indicators are:
- a reduction in smoking uptake rates among teenagers who have participated in an education project
- a new pharmacy ordering system has been implemented and is functioning at specified standards (timeliness, accuracy etc.)
- a new way of triaging Emergency Department patients results in improved patient satisfaction.

Questions for designing process and impact evaluation

It can be useful to think about process and impact evaluation together when designing a project evaluation. Taken together, process and impact evaluation assess how the project went and what it produced, providing important learning about the project's planning and implementation. Fundamentally, process and impact evaluation aim to answer the following five key questions:

1. How well did we do what we said we would do?
2. What worked and what didn't and why?
3. What difference did it make that we did this?
4. What could we do differently?
5. What can be learned from the project to improve practice and inform other projects?

Table 6.2 provides examples of ways of breaking down and exploring answers to the key evaluation questions.

Table 6.2 Process and impact evaluation questions breakdown

Key evaluation questions	Breakdown of questions
1) How well did we do what we said we would do?	• Have all planned project tasks and activities been completed? • How well has the project achieved its goal and objectives? • If the objectives changed during the project, how and why did they change? • Has the project developed resources suitable for future use? • Have the skills of project team members been developed as a result of the project? • What partnerships have the project team formed to enhance capacity and capability?
2) What worked and what didn't and why?	• What strategies worked well or didn't work well for involving the target population or staff? Why? • What strategies worked well or didn't work well for acquiring support from key stakeholders of the project? Why? • Have any of the activities and strategies been changed? Why? • Which of the project goals and objectives were fully achieved? • Did they comprehensively address the problem that gave rise to the project? • In what ways did the project planning process work most effectively?
3) What difference did it make that we did this?	• Has the project led to changes in, for example, knowledge, attitude, skills and behaviour among target population or key stakeholders? • Did the project have any unexpected impacts? • What evidence is there to attribute results to the project? • Were other initiatives started, alternative services proposed or new funding resources acquired as a result of the project? • Are the outcomes of the project sustainable, and will the new intervention or service continue beyond the initial funding? • To what extent is the new intervention or service model/approach transferable to other organisations, settings or communities?

Table 6.2 Process and Impact Evaluation questions breakdown *continued*

Key evaluation questions	Breakdown of questions
4) What could we do differently?	• Are there more effective ways to achieve the objectives that emerged during the life of the project? • What additional resources, skills or knowledge are needed to do projects like this one more effectively? • What additional support from stakeholders such as financial sponsors would have been useful to the project in meeting its goals and objectives? • How could we have improved stakeholder engagement? • Have we identified a better way of developing realistic goals and objectives in the initial planning stage? • Could the project results be made more widely available to others?
5) What can be learned from the project to improve practice and inform other projects?	• How will project findings be used for future knowledge development? • What have we learned about doing evaluation? • How will the evaluation results be made available for new project planning? • How will the project outcomes be used to influence policy and research priorities?

Outcome evaluation

Outcome evaluation measures the longer-term results or benefits of the project, and is usually done after the project has been completed for a defined period. Impact and outcome evaluation both assess the effects of the completed project, but over different time periods. However, outcome evaluation is virtually impossible in the timeframes that apply to projects. See Case 6.1 for an example of three types of evaluation in the community setting.

Case 6.1 Evaluation in the community setting

A community health service had a request from a local general practitioner (GP) concerning the needs of an increasing number of Afghani women attending her surgery. She felt that their needs were largely social and emotional rather than medical, and asked,

'Could you do something for them?' The agency met with the women's unofficial interpreter, and after much discussion set up a project to establish an Afghani Women's Health Project in the area with the following **three project objectives:**

1) Provide Afghani women with opportunities to voice their health needs.

2) Raise awareness among participants about the services available that can meet their needs and provide effective referral pathways.

3) Engage local service providers in providing care and support to Afghani women to meet their health needs.

The following key project strategies were implemented and activities were completed: discussion groups were held, resources were collected, and an Afghani Women's Health Forum was conducted, with invited speakers addressing important cultural and health issues. Other activities followed. Service providers in the area took part, and were successfully engaged in broader responses to the needs of the group.

The project was evaluated in several ways. As the project leader said: 'First, we asked the question "Did we do what we set out to do—that is, did we successfully establish the project?" The answer to that question was clearly yes. Second, we collected data on the numbers of women and service providers attending all the activities, and we collected demographic data about the range of women attending—age, education, etc. Third, we asked for feedback from all participants in our activities through both participant feedback sheets and group discussion. Finally, we involved the Afghani women in decision-making about future activities, thus reflecting on what we had done and identifying what worked and what didn't. In this way, we carried out both process and impact evaluation—we just did what seemed logical.'

An outcome evaluation of the project—that is, of its contribution to the better health of the women involved—was not possible, because the timeframe and the complexity of measuring health outcomes were beyond its scope. However, the project had both unforeseen and longer-term impacts. For example, the women identified a whole range of issues as important to their health, such as housing, immigration, work and education, which went well beyond the issues the agency had initially considered. The women also organised among themselves and became very involved in local housing issues. One woman went on to open her own restaurant, actively supported by the others.

There was also an impact on service providers, who were made aware of the group's needs and priorities. They realised that some of their normal practice should be changed if they were to meet the needs of such a group. This realisation led to a series of cultural awareness projects in some of the mainstream agencies.

But there was another way the staff knew that the project had been a success. 'When they came to hold their meetings, they filled the place up with laughter, colour, food and good energy. That good energy lifted the spirits of everyone else in the place—hard to explain in evaluation terms but easy to see and feel in practice.'

Evaluation approaches and design

In this section, we explain the major approaches to project evaluation. Because each project is different, the choice of method/s is quite broad—the only constant is the need to plan your evaluation so that the right evaluation questions are asked at the right time, allowing the right information to be collected in the right way for that project as part of its implementation. Project evaluation needs to be methodical and to produce valid conclusions based on reliable data or observations, but the scope and complexity will be tailored to the needs of the project and its stakeholders, and it usually doesn't need to meet the standards of traditional scientific research.

There are many methods and data collection techniques that can be used. This is likely to include 'hard' or quantitative data such as occupational health and safety or workforce statistics, and data on performance (such as time-to-treat standards for emergency care) as well as the softer, more qualitative approaches. As Patton (1990, p. 9) argues:

There are no rigid rules that can be provided for making data collection and methods decisions in evaluation. The art of evaluation involves creating a design and gathering information that is appropriate for a specific situation and a policy-making context.

Clinical care improvement projects will generally use some traditional quantitative data to measure the impact of changes on the effectiveness or timeliness or cost of care. But when projects are seeking to introduce new ways of approaching complex social problems (for example, family violence), where the social, legal, economic and cultural context are important influences on what will work and how, methods such as 'realist evaluation' (Pawson & Tilley 1997) and other interpretive approaches such as the Theory of Change approach are needed (Chen 1990; Chen 2011; Wadsworth 2010). While these methods often include quantitative data, they generally emphasise qualitative methods including interviews with key players, direct and indirect observation, focus groups and case studies. We explain one theory-based approach to designing project evaluation in detail below.

Program logic model

The program logic model is a framework for planning and evaluating programs in the social, health, environment and international development fields. It is usually presented as in Figure 6.1, showing the relationships between the goals of a program, the required inputs and processes, the outputs, and the intended impact (short-term benefits) and outcomes (long-term benefits). To use this framework, the first requirement is that the 'theory' (or logic) of the program is made explicit, including the causal relationships between the elements.

While the program logic model is not often cited in the general project management literature, it is used for projects that develop and trial a new intervention or activity, or to evaluate an existing program. Its advantages are the focus on clarifying the assumed cause and effect relationships (thus making it possible to test them) and the presentation of the overall logic of the program in a single diagram.

The program logic model is used to understand the program or project design: certain resources (inputs—such as a budget, staff, facilities, supplies) are allocated to enable certain activities to be undertaken

Figure 6.1 Program logic and evaluation

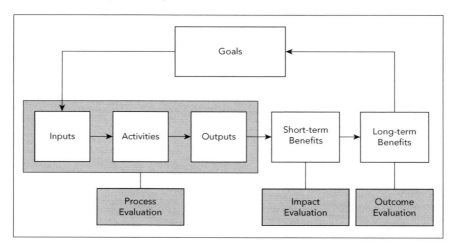

(for example, diagnosis, treatment and support for self-management for people with diabetes in an area), which produce certain outputs (numbers of people diagnosed, treated, etc.), which have measurable impacts (e.g. controlled levels of sugar in the blood) that can be predicted to lead to health benefits or outcomes (slower progress of the disease, fewer hospitalisations, more active and longer lives). It is often used as a framework for evaluating population health programs because it clarifies the cause–effect relationships between observed elements and the achievement of the program goals, and thus what to measure and what indicators to use. Most importantly, it helps evaluators to analyse the reasons for success or failure, by focusing on where the program's work may not have addressed the necessary cause–effect relationships (for example, by under-resourcing an essential activity, or executing it poorly or not enough for the needed effect).

A program logic model for a project does not replace the detailed project plan. Rather, it enables the logic of the project as an intervention to be made explicit and provides the basis for an evaluation plan.

Benefits realisation

Another way of considering project outcomes and evaluating project success, particularly in relation to ICT projects, is **benefits realisation**. A benefit can be defined as a net positive change in outcomes, including patient care and health or wellbeing outcomes. The preparation of a benefits realisation plan (which defines expected benefits and sets targets) and its formal use in the governance of the project is a way of increasing the chances that the benefit will actually be delivered (NSW Government 2018). Put simply, a benefits realisation plan is a tool to make sure you get the intended benefit originally planned for your project (NHS Institute for Innovation and Improvement 2008).

The decision to implement clinical information systems and electronic medical records (EMRs) is often funded based on a proposal (or **business case**) that specifies anticipated benefits. For example, for electronic ordering of pathology and radiology tests, one of the expected benefits would be a reduced number of inappropriate or duplicate tests ordered. For electronic prescribing, the expected benefits would include faster supply of medications and a reduction in medication errors. Benefits can be bankable (they can enable dollar savings, for example in consumables or space) or non-bankable—in the form of productivity gains (for example, time savings) or improved patient satisfaction. It should be noted that benefits are often not realised until some time after the project has been completed, and realisation plans often monitor benefit over a three- to five-year period.

PRINCE2® includes a benefit realisation framework (Axelos 2017), which has been used in major ICT projects by the National Health Service (NHS) in the United Kingdom. According to the NHS, the value of focusing on benefits realisation planning is that you can track whether intended benefits have been realised and sustained after the end of the project. It also helps to ensure a clear signposting of who is responsible for the delivery of those benefits (NHS Institute for Innovation and Improvement 2008). Like other evaluation planning, a benefits realisation plan is often developed early, at the same time as the business case, and updated in the planning phase. A benefits realisation plan typically contains the following information:

- the key outcomes (or benefits) of the project
- the benefit type (bankable, productivity or health gain)
- baseline and target measures to be achieved for each benefit
- the expected delivery schedule for each benefit
- an overview of the monitoring capabilities required to measure each specified benefit, along with details explaining how each capability will be delivered

- an explanation of the risks that may threaten the achievement of each benefit, and how the threat will be handled.

The NSW government's Benefits Realisation Management Framework is a well-documented approach (available at www.finance.nsw. gov.au/publication-and-resources/benefits-realisation-management-framework) and provides a clear guide describing benefits management principles, processes, templates and guidelines including implementation.

Evaluation planning and the seven-step approach

An essential part of project planning is to determine how and when activities and achievement of milestones need to be assessed (sometimes known as 'tracking' in project jargon). The project plan will have defined and itemised the project goals and objectives, activities, quality standards and expected benefits (see Chapters 4 and 5), and these provide the bedrock for evaluation. Most projects will need both process and impact evaluation. A process evaluation plan should outline the questions of interest regarding the project's progress and outputs, and specify the stages at which they are to be considered, how and by whom. An impact evaluation plan should outline the standards, targets or outcomes against which the project will be measured; how the measurement will be made; and who will be involved.

Like most major tasks, evaluation planning is best approached in a logical, step-by-step way. To conduct evaluation smoothly and successfully, especially for complex projects, a structured approach is recommended. Table 6.3 explains a structured approach in seven steps.

Table 6.4 applies the seven-step approach to a case study that evaluated the establishment of an on-site primary care clinic in a large American manufacturing company that bears the costs of some health care for employees (Griffith and Strasser 2010).

For long, complex projects with multiple strategies, the use of evaluation templates that provide summative views of what is required and by when can make the evaluation plan easier to understand and follow. Templates for use in planning process and impact evaluations are provided at the end of the book (Template 6.1 and 6.2).

Economic evaluation

Economic evaluation is concerned with estimating the relative value of alternative options, and is designed to help decision-makers answer the

Table 6.3 Evaluation in seven steps

Step	Focus	Details
1.	Definition of work	Review key strategies and activities that are to be conducted and the expected immediate and longer-term benefits
2.	Development of evaluation questions and success indicators	Develop questions, targets and indicators of success that can be used to measure the completion and quality of the activities and also the defined benefits
3.	Selection of methods	Determine methods to be used to collect data for each target and success indicator
4.	Allocation of responsibility and tasks	Decide who will be responsible for the overall evaluation, and who will undertake the tasks involved
5.	Set timeline	Determine the timeline for collection of different types of data
6.	Data analysis and interpretation	Analyse the data and interpret its meaning to answer each of the evaluation questions
7.	Dissemination and application of results	Write an evaluation report that can be shared among the team, within the organisation and with key stakeholders including funding bodies. Consider presenting the results at conferences and publishing in journals. Consider how the results and learning can be available to be applied in future project and evaluation design.

question: Is this service/program/intervention worth doing compared with other things we could do with these same resources? It can be an important approach to evaluation of projects that introduce new ways of providing care or services.

Economic evaluation is the comparison of alternative options in terms of their costs and consequences (Gray & Wilkinson 2016). It focuses on project input versus output, cost versus consequences, and provides evidence to compare and choose between alternatives (Drummond et al. 2015). For example, in order to answer the four questions listed in Table 6.5, different types of information collected via various processes/methods may be required.

Table 6.4 Seven-step evaluation example—piloting an on-site primary care clinic

Step	Details
1. Definition of work	To pilot an on-site clinic that provides employees with primary health care, health promotion and disease prevention services, including screening, early diagnosis and treatment. The ultimate goal is to significantly reduce the company's health care costs and lost-productivity costs. The pilot will be evaluated after one year.
2. Development of evaluation questions and success indicators	Clinic utilisation What are average daily patient numbers 6 months and 12 months after the opening of the clinic? • Average daily number of patient attendances for each type of service Return on investment (ROI) What costs were avoided as a result of the on-site clinic? • Complete costs for all on-site services provided • Estimated cost for equivalent primary care services if provided externally What is the average monthly sick leave reduction in the past 12 months? • The difference between the number of sick leave days as a result of attending external primary care services in the 12 months prior to the provision of on-site clinic and the number of sick leave days taken during the 12 months of the pilot Employee satisfaction How acceptable is the on-site clinic to employees who used the service? • Mean score of employee willingness to continue attending the on-site clinic, measured using a 5 point Likert scale How likely are employees to recommend the on-site clinic to others? • Mean score of employee willingness to recommend the service to others, measured using a 5 point Likert scale
3. Selection of methods	For clinic utilisation, records will be kept of all attendances and services provided by the on-site clinic. For ROI, comparison costing of equivalent services provided elsewhere will be estimated based on primary care fees and charges (using disease classification) by external service providers over the preceding 12 months.

	Costs of the clinic will be available from internal cost-centre accounts. For the sick leave saved, HR records of attendance and sick leave data over two years will be used.
4. Allocation of responsibility and tasks	Project consultant and his team will be in charge of conducting the evaluation, including data collection and analysis.
5. Set timeline	Data in relation to the past sick leave and external service access and costs will be collected prior to the commencement of the on-site clinic. Other data will be collected monthly and analysed following the 6th and 12th months of the project. Questionnaires on 'willingness' will be collected upon patients' completion of the course of service/treatment.
6. Data analysis and interpretation	All data are quantitative, so appropriate quantitative methods of determining totals and means will be used.
7. Dissemination and application of results	Evaluation consultant will hold focus group discussions with all project staff, on-site clinical service providers and senior management to discuss any difficulties encountered and lessons learned from the pilot project. Report will be provided to company management, covering benefits of the on-site clinic and focusing on the three major measurements, on lessons learned, recommendations for or against continuation, and design of future approach.

Table 6.5 Economic evaluation questions

Question One:
Should clinicians check the blood pressure of each adult who walks into their offices?

Question Two:
Should a community service take on providing settlement help for newly arrived immigrants and refugees?

Question Three:
Should hospital administrators purchase each piece of new diagnostic equipment proven beneficial for fast and accurate diagnosis?

Question Four:
Should an organisation introduce a new system for monitoring adverse events that will cost $4.3 million to install and $0.6 million each year to operate?

Source: Adapted from Drummond et al. 2015, p. 1.

Typically, answers to these questions are most strongly influenced by our estimates of the relative merit or value of the alternative course of action they pose. Because funding for health and social care is always limited, considerations of relative value become paramount. Are the benefits—for individuals or the population—worth the costs, as compared to other uses of that money? What if demand is higher than predicted?

The principle is that resource allocation decisions should maximise efficient use of resources (Drummond et al. 2015). In order to provide reliable guidance on this question for health or community service delivery, decision-makers also need information on the related questions of:

- **Efficacy**—can it work in testing, and to what extent?
- Effectiveness—will it work in this specific environment and for this specific group of people?
- Acceptability—will the people who are the intended recipients accept it?
- Accessibility—will it reach those who need it?

Methods of economic evaluation of interventions or services include three main types: **cost–benefit analysis** (CBA), **cost–effectiveness analysis** (CEA) and **cost–utility analysis** (CUA). The difference between them can be confusing. *Cost-benefit analysis* estimates (in dollars) the costs and benefits of a given intervention compared with another intervention. In recent years, cost-benefit analysis has been criticised precisely because it reduces complex values, such as quality of life, to dollar figures. *Cost-effectiveness analysis* and *cost-utility analysis* express outcomes in non-monetary terms. CEA uses 'natural units' such as cure rate or reduction in the incidence of a disease. CUA attempts to express outcomes in quality-adjusted life years (QALYs) so that comparisons of benefit can be made between alternative conditions or service types. Table 6.6 provides some details of these three types of evaluation in terms of their measurements of costs and consequences.

Economic evaluation is normally carried out by health or welfare economists, who assume that resources are scarce and see economic valuation as an aid to rational allocation of resources. This type of evaluation uses concepts such as opportunity cost—achieving one sort of benefit at the expense of other benefits forgone—and marginal analysis—making decisions on the relationship between the last dollar spent on a program

Table 6.6 Economic evaluation—measurement of costs versus consequences

Type of study	Measurement of costs	Indicators of consequences	Measurement/ valuation of consequences
Cost-benefit analysis	Monetary units	Single or multiple effects, not necessarily common to both alternatives	Monetary units
Cost-effectiveness analysis	Monetary units	Single effect of interest, common to both alternatives, but achieved to different degrees	Natural units (e.g. life years gained, disability days saved, points of blood pressure reduction)
Cost-utility analysis	Monetary units	Single or multiple effects, not necessarily common to both alternatives	Healthy years (typically measured as QALYs)

Source: Drummond et al. 2015, p. 11

or intervention and the benefit received for that dollar—rather than focusing on the average benefit of the program (Meacock et al. 2014). Economic evaluation assesses the relative soundness and efficiency of interventions (Drummond et al. 2015; Gray & Wilkinson 2016) and 'in theory allows decision makers to be more rational in determining which projects to fund or expand and which to cut or contract' (Carter & Harris 1999, p. 154).

Post-Implementation Review

A **Post-Implementation Review (PIR)** is conducted after completing a project. Its purpose is to evaluate whether project objectives were met, to determine how effectively the project was run, to learn lessons for the future, and to ensure that the organisation gets the greatest possible benefit from the project (see www.mindtools.com). A PIR may be conducted by an objective third party; it should include evaluation from the perspectives of stakeholders, and also use information from earlier evaluation activities.

In planning for a PIR, consideration should be given to the method and questions that will be asked, as there are many ways to gather the information you want to determine what worked and what didn't in your project. Westland (2018) offers some examples:

- **Gap analysis.** This method of assessing how a plan differed from the actual application is always a powerful tool to see what benchmarks you met, and which you didn't.
- **Project goals.** Simply put, did you achieve the goals of your project? Are your deliverables functioning as planned? What was the error rate of the project?
- **Stakeholders.** How satisfied are your stakeholders? Were users' needs met?
- **Cost.** How much did the project end up costing? What are the costs involved in operating the project's result?
- **Benefits.** Did the project achieve the benefits projected, and if not why and how can that be improved?
- **Lessons.** What went well, and what can you learn from that experience?
- **Report.** Document what you learned from the review.

Consideration as to the timing of a PIR is also important—long enough after project completion that the results have truly taken effect, but soon enough that those involved still have fresh memories.

Collecting and using data

Some ways of collecting data are more intrusive for the people involved, and generally more costly to collect, than others. In addition to collecting data from primary sources (which usually requires direct interaction with people), data from secondary sources (that is, existing data collections) can also be used, perhaps requiring new analysis. (See Chapter 4, Table 4.5 for examples of these two types of data sources).

Depending on the complexity of the project and the type of evaluation questions, mixed methods and sources are often used. For example, for evaluating a training project, the number of training sessions and number of attendees will be available from training records. However, if we need to know the quality and benefits of the training session, then questionnaires or interviews on participant satisfaction and/or measures of improved competence in practice are needed, but harder to collect.

Both qualitative and quantitative data need to be relevant, accurately collected and recorded, and valid indicators of the things they are used to measure. And if cause and effect relationships are to be attributed (for example, if an improvement in the mental health of carers is to be claimed as a result of a project to increase access to respite services), then care must be taken to eliminate other possible reasons for the improvement (for example, the carers pension was increased at the same time). For more information on this and other methods questions, please see the readings and resources at the end of this chapter.

External or internal evaluation

Project evaluation can be carried out by the project team themselves—'insider evaluation'—with input from the key stakeholders. For the people involved, participation in evaluation assists in the process of finishing and moving on. Insider evaluation has the benefit of the participants' intimate knowledge and understanding of the project. It can encourage the development of critical reflection skills and assist in embedding these skills within the organisation. However, insider evaluation might be less rigorous because of lack of evaluation expertise, or because of bias, since participants may want their project to look good and will dwell more on the positives. This can mean that the results of insider evaluation are viewed as being invalid or of less value than evaluation by others.

Evaluation is often carried out by external evaluators, perhaps a group of skilled specialists in a particular method or approach (for example, economic evaluation), particularly for complex or large projects. But some of the benefits of fresh eyes and objectivity can be acquired when expert staff from other parts of the organisation, who are not part of the project team, are engaged as evaluators. Table 6.7 summarises the benefits and limitations of conducting insider versus outsider evaluation.

Evaluation in practice—challenges and learning

Early preparation for evaluation, and building in data collection, reflection and review during the project, will enable the organisation to assess the project's impact, or at least its outputs, based on clear criteria and hopefully some solid evidence. It can also enable significant learning about how and why the project succeeded (or not), with potential benefit to the organisation's innovation capability. However, resistance to undertaking a formal project evaluation is common for several reasons.

Table 6.7 Insider versus outsider evaluation

Insiders doing the evaluation	Outsiders doing the evaluation
Benefits • Can have a deep understanding of the project and its context • Likely to develop trust with staff and community groups involved • Part of the organisational structure • A way of developing evaluation skills, critical reflection • Less costly *Limitations* • Difficulties in recruiting internal staff • May not have time to devote to evaluation • May lack skills and experience required to design and implement an evaluation • Role conflict or organisation loyalty may impede objectivity and reduce credibility of findings	*Benefits* • Bring outsiders' perspective and objectivity, might more readily make tough recommendations • Can be viewed by funders as providing more independence, free from organisational bias • Can provide a fresh look at the project • Bring evaluation expertise and experience from other evaluations • Can act as facilitator between participants and stakeholders • Can bring organisation into contact with additional technical resources *Limitations* • Higher costs • Might have less knowledge of the project and organisational and political environment • May require time to develop trust among staff and participants • Time required for negotiating contracts and for orientation and monitoring

Project reviews are sometimes instigated without specific objectives, or for 'political' motives (that is, reasons arising from power issues within the organisation).

For example, an opportunity to evaluate a project that has made an unwelcome change in the role of a group of staff could become their chance to take revenge—resistance does not necessarily stop at the project's closing party. On the other hand, looking transparently at things that went wrong or need improvement, even with the best of intentions, is very confronting and tends to be avoided. The pressure to focus on the next goal or task also contributes.

Although evaluation frameworks are sometimes provided by governments or other funders to guide evaluation design, there is no one-size-fits-all approach. Even a well-designed evaluation strategy may bring difficult challenges for project staff, especially when inadequate training and preparation for completing evaluation tasks are provided. Some challenges are specific to the health and community service sectors, including the use of interventions intended to address complex social and health problems. Both understanding and demonstrating cause and effect between a service and the impact on patients or participants can be particularly difficult (Pawson & Tilley 1997). Demonstrating the impact of illness prevention projects is sometimes even harder, and it may be necessary to use indirect or intermediate benefits as indicators. Sometimes, evaluation can only provide good quality information rather than ready-made answers to inform decision-making (Larsen et al. 2005). The engagement of many diverse stakeholders in health and community services projects can also bring challenges for project evaluation.

Yet it is important to learn from project processes and outcomes, and evaluation provides a way to crystallise the learning and formulate desired changes in approach or method. Otherwise, the short-term nature of projects provides the perfect setting for reinventing the wheel (wasting energy and time) and repeating errors (reducing the chances of success). And when the project has a direct impact on patient or client care, monitoring and review are essential to assess the impact and ensure there are no adverse effects on standards or access for the client population.

Summary

- Evaluation is a way of understanding whether a project has done what it planned to do, whether it produced the intended benefits, and why or why not.
- Evaluation is one of the tools to generate knowledge and evidence to guide the sector in better services, programs and project design.
- Process evaluation, impact evaluation and outcome evaluation are three common types of formal evaluation aimed at answering different questions and developing a better understanding of both the conduct and the achievements of the project. Benefits realisation is a new method that has similar aims.

- The program logic model is a framework for planning and evaluation, used in the social, health, environment and international development fields. It depicts the relationships between the goals of a project or program, the required inputs and processes, the outputs and the intended impact.
- Evaluation planning is best approached in a logical, step-by-step way. We recommend a structured seven-step approach.
- Economic evaluation is a method for weighing up the costs and the value of alternative interventions or initiatives, and can provide important evidence for health and social care projects.
- Post-Implementation Review is undertaken after a project is complete, to assist organisations to ensure they realise the potential value of projects.

Readings and resources

Gray, A.M. & Wilkinson, T., 2016, 'Economic evaluation of healthcare interventions: old and new directions', *Oxford Review of Economic Policy*, vol. 32, no. 1, pp. 102–21

Larsen, L., Cummins, J., Brown, H., Ajmal, T., Beers, H. & Lee, J., 2005, *Learning from Evaluation: Summary of reports of evaluations of leadership initiatives*, London: Office for Public Management/NHS Leadership Centre

Pawson, R. & Tilley, N., 1997, *Realistic Evaluation*, London: SAGE Publications

Pinto, J.K. & Slevin, D.P., 1988, 'Critical success factors across the project life cycle: Definitions and measurement techniques', *Project Management Journal*, vol. 19, no. 3, pp. 67–75

Piperca, S. & Floricel, S., 2012, 'A typology of unexpected events in complex projects', *International Journal of Managing Projects in Business*, vol. 5, no. 2, pp. 248–65

Post-Implementation Review: www.mindtools.com/pages/article/newPPM_74.htm

South Australian Community Health Research Unit (SACHRU), 2008, 'Planning and evaluation wizard', Flinders University, Adelaide, www.flinders.edu.au/medicine/sites/pew/pew_home.cfm

7

Planning tools: scheduling, budgeting and the business case

Chapter outline

Work breakdown structure: tasks, sequencing and timing
    Key components of WBS
    Constructing a WBS
Estimating time, and using scheduling tools
    Gantt charting
Budgeting
    Budget development
    Identifying and estimating costs
    Direct and indirect costs
    Getting the budget right: not too little, not too much
    The golden rule of budgeting
    Budget items
    Sources of funding and other resources
    Constructing a detailed budget
    Budgeting for contingencies

> The project business case
>   Writing a business case
>   What about projects with no positive business case?
> Summary
> Readings and resources

In this chapter, we focus on planning the timing, activities and resources needed for projects—the core of the work program—and the technical tools that make it possible. They are worth knowing, as they can be powerful aids to demystifying the 'when, how and how much?' questions that can otherwise seem too hard to answer. We also explain the related strategy of developing a business case.

Work breakdown structure: tasks, sequencing and timing

A journey of a thousand miles starts from beneath one's feet.
(Lao Tse 1963, p. 125)

The WBS is 'a tool that the project team uses progressively to divide the work of a project into smaller and smaller pieces' (Kloppenborg 2009, p. 142). It enables the project manager and the team to:
- develop a full appreciation of the scope and sequencing of the project
- document all the tasks and activities that have to be completed
- identify the resources required to complete the tasks
- see the relationships and dependencies between the tasks
- identify milestones **and track progress against a timeline**
- more accurately estimate the time required for the project and specify any deadlines (or critical points).

Project strategies cannot be implemented unless there is a clear action plan, with the necessary staff, resources and equipment at hand. The activities and tasks of a project need to be defined and broken down into manageable chunks, and the simplest way to do this is to start with the goals, strategies and deliverables identified in the project charter. You can then break them down using subheadings and expand on them in a list format. In project management terms, this is called creating a

work breakdown structure (WBS). The concept of the WBS was initially developed by the United States Department of Defense in 1962 (Hamilton 1964) and has been widely used in all defence services since, spreading gradually to other fields (Haugan 2003). The process of building a good WBS forces significant issues to arise early rather than later in a project, and also provides the basis for estimating the time and cost of the overall project. In fact, the WBS is a powerful tool for expressing the scope of a project in a simple graphical format.

There are many techniques and rules of thumb for developing the WBS that can help with sizing the tasks and defining the relationships between them, as well as with other technical aspects. Some tasks may take a long time to complete, but are simple and straightforward. Some tasks require specialised knowledge and skills, some need to be managed independently and others require teamwork. Identifying and detailing the tasks can be difficult, and the ideas will probably flow faster if it is done by the team or a working group rather than an individual. A good WBS provides a clear picture of the sequence of all project tasks to be completed, and enables the team to estimate the time and intensity of tasks, and to develop a better understanding of what skills are required and who can best get the work done.

Key components of WBS

A WBS is a hierarchical structure with a single 'box' at the top representing the whole project, as shown in Figure 7.1. The project is then divided into components fitting into the lower levels of boxes in the WBS diagram. It apportions the entire project into logical chunks of work, which are then subdivided and arranged in the right order (Hill 2010).

The second level of the WBS is the deliverables—the products or outputs that together represent everything the project must achieve (Hill 2010). Getting the statement of deliverables right is important at this stage, as they are the organising principle for the rest of the WBS. A statement of deliverables from the project plan or charter provides the basis, but it may need a little refinement for the purposes of the WBS, as the project team gets closer to the question of what project strategies can really deliver.

Each deliverable will require a number of activities to be conducted. Activity is the next level down in the WBS. An activity is basically a

Figure 7.1 WBS subdivided into boxes

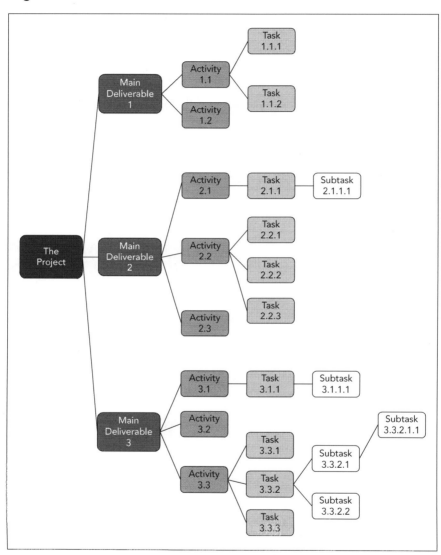

manageable collection of related tasks that contribute to a single deliverable (Hill 2010). Each activity in turn will require the completion of a set of tasks. These categories (tasks and activities) are highly variable depending on the scope and needs of the project (a small project's activity may be a larger project's task), and in some ways are defined by their relationship to one another and to the higher levels of the WBS. Thus tasks are discrete pieces of work that are needed to complete a single activity.

A **work package** includes all the scheduled activities and tasks (with milestones) that are required to complete a deliverable in a WBS (Kloppenborg 2009). A work package should be detailed enough to facilitate further planning, such as scheduling tasks and determining resources, and to assist the project manager to maintain control of time and resource use during implementation.

Constructing a WBS

The common steps are logical: start with the deliverables, break each one into meaningful activities, and then into tasks, in descending order. It is important that each element in the WBS is described clearly, but briefly.

The WBS is usually presented in a graphic format. Figure 7.1 shows a vertical WBS, with deliverables listed on the left and dropping from top to bottom. Activities are listed in a column to the right of each deliverable, and tasks follow the same format. The work represented in this way for each deliverable is sometimes called a '**deliverable leg**'. A WBS can be presented in many other formats, including horizontally (with deliverables listed on the top from left to right) and can be shown in outline only (Hill 2010).

The WBS can also be presented in project stages, or according to responsibilities (such as for different team members or groups). Display by stages is used for multistage projects, and the deliverables for each stage are grouped. Display-by-responsibilities brings together the activities for which individuals or groups (often with specific skills) are likely to be responsible. These different ways of presenting the WBS will suit the needs of different projects, users and audiences.

Normally, two or three activities for each deliverable are enough (Hill 2010), but there are no standard rules for this—you just need to be able to visualise the sequence of events. It can be hard to know when to stop dividing an activity into smaller elements. One rule of thumb is the **80–hour rule** (Kliem et al. 1997): no single activity or group of tasks should require more than 80 hours (or two weeks) of work. But this rule may not always apply, depending on the nature of the project, its activities, and the skill and experience of the project team.

Another way of thinking about this question is to make sure that activities are set so that they don't last longer than the time between meetings of the project board or committee. This way, regular progress reports will be clear, tracking and monitoring easier, and the team will have some achievements to report. So the best rule is the common sense rule—be as detailed as makes sense for the project team.

We have described above the top-down approach to constructing a WBS, but it can also be approached bottom-up—that is, by identifying all the work elements first and then grouping them to form the higher levels (Hill 2010). In reality, the process often involves a mix of the two—as you specify activities and tasks, any omissions or errors in the way the deliverables have been described come to light, and can be corrected. The WBS in Figure 7.1 is displayed according to 'deliverables' or 'products' of the project.

The construction of a WBS and the specification of individual work packages allows time, cost, schedule and even associated risks to be estimated individually, and also enables responsibilities to be allocated to project team members. Table 7.1 details one of the work packages in the WBS for a project that aims to reduce steroid use among high school students.

Estimating time, and using scheduling tools

Managing time is important for projects, and estimating the time required for tasks and activities is a reliable way to establish a schedule and milestones against which progress can be assessed (Kliem et al. 1997; Martin 2002). The development of the WBS gives you a starting point for performing the next difficult task of project planning: estimating the time required to complete each task and the whole project. This is best done bottom-up—that is, by firstly estimating the time required for each task and work package (Kloppenborg 2009). In principle, the summation of the time required for the completion of all work packages gives you the estimate of time required for the completion of the project. However, some work packages or tasks can be undertaken in parallel, so the whole may be less than the sum of the parts. It is also important to remember that the three factors—time, cost and quality—must be considered together. Time estimates can't be finalised without reference to cost and quality considerations.

The challenges in estimating time requirements relate to four factors. Firstly, some tasks may require specialised skills and expertise, which

Table 7.1 Work package example

Project aim: To reduce the prevalence of androgenic anabolic steroid misuse among grade 10 public school students in the City Council Area	Deliverables: 80% of a sample of grade 10 public school male students in the City Council Area improve scores on Adolescent Appearance Distress Scale.		
Activities	Resources	Duration and work time	Cost
Conduct survey of current appearance distress scores	Project team leader Project officer Teachers	2 months (60 hrs) 2 months (160 hrs) 1 month (20 hrs)	
Conduct promotional campaign	Project officer Printing services Teachers	2 months (85 hrs) 1 month 15 hours	
Facilitate series of group discussions among 200 grade 10 male and female students to encourage positive and effective communications	Project officer Project team leader Teachers	6 months (0.7FTE) 6 months (70 hrs) 5 months (300 hrs)	
Repeat survey of appearance distress scores	Project team leader Project officer Teachers	2 months (20 hrs) 2 months (160 hrs) 1 month (20 hrs)	
Facilitate series of workshops for 200 grade 10 students to consolidate and advance changes (in the second year of the project)	Project officer Project team leader Teachers	8 months (260 hrs) 8 months (85 hrs) 5 months (300 hrs)	

makes it hard for non-experts to estimate the complexity and therefore the time required. Secondly, good estimation requires a substantial investment of time and energy, which may be exactly what is lacking in project planning. Thirdly, differences between senior management and project staff regarding expectations and quality requirements can complicate this task, as can a lack of support or involvement by management and key stakeholders in the planning process. Finally, financial constraints also challenge both the planning and execution of projects.

One of the common mistakes made during estimation is overestimating the productivity of project staff (Roberts 2011). If non-productive time is not taken into consideration during estimation, the timescale for project completion won't be realistic. There will inevitably be tasks that are necessary but not directly related to the building blocks in the WBS. Industries other than health and community services often use a standard productivity rate of between 56 per cent and 80 per cent (Roberts 2011) to recognise these factors. On the other hand, overestimating the time needed for the completion of the project is equally undesirable, and it is worth examining the time allowed for individual tasks to find and remove unnecessary padding (Goldratt 1994).

In the case of small projects, some form of brainstorming with colleagues may be a good approach. For large-scale and complex projects, estimates can be tested by seeking second opinions—by talking to people who are not involved in the project but have had experience in similar projects. You can also use estimates from projects that are similar to yours as a guide.

Even though estimating can be hard, putting time and resources into it means you are more likely to avoid unsuccessful project implementation.

Gantt charting

The Gantt chart is one of the oldest project management tools, and one of the most commonly used methods of presenting schedule information (and of charting actual progress). A Gantt chart plots activities (in rows) against the timeline (in columns), thus showing the relationships between them. Gantt charts can also show the resources required for a particular task or activity, as well as the relationships between the tasks, milestones and baselines; and can be used to track planned and actual progress (Meredith & Mantel 2012). Figure 7.2 presents a simple Gantt chart for the project of conducting a community survey.

For a simple project, a Gantt chart may be produced using a simple table format; for more complex projects, an application such as Microsoft Project software is needed. Gantt charts are useful in both the planning and implementation phases of the project, because they are simple, easily understood and very effective for showing the status of a task or a group of tasks against the schedule. Their limitations include the fact that they can be difficult to update if there are lots of changes and can be hard to manage in more complex projects.

Figure 7.2 Simple Gantt chart

	Task name	Duration	April	May	June	July
1	Literature review	20 days				
2	Conduct survey	39 days				
2.1	Prepare questionnaire	10 days				
2.2	Pilot questionnaire	7 days				
2.3	Review questionnaire	7 days				
2.4	Interviews	15 days				
7	Analyse results	15 days				
8	Write report	65 days				
8.1	Structure and outline	5 days				
8.2	First draft	27 days				
8.3	Second draft	12 days				
9	Release of report	0 days				18/07

The many other project management charting and scheduling techniques include network diagrams, critical path analysis (which shows the critical tasks and times for the project to meet a deadline), and the **program evaluation and review technique** (PERT), one of the first formal methods developed for scheduling projects. They are not as often used in health and community services, other than in some building and ICT projects, because there is often not the same focus on managing technical tasks and resources concurrently. Descriptions and tips on how to use them are included in many texts and available online.

Larger and more complex projects are often better handled in stages. This is helpful when there are major unknowns which will only be clarified as the project progresses, or when there is major risk that needs to be mitigated. For example, building and ICT system implementation projects are often divided into stages due to their size and complexity. Projects that aim to design and test new models of care, on the other hand, may be organised in stages because the testing process can't be determined until the design is known. Similarly, in research projects, the results of earlier stages of the study will often shape the later stages. Structuring projects in stages—where design/redesign in the light of learnings from the previous stage is a planned strategy—can be an essential aid to maintaining quality, momentum and control.

Some of the breaks between stages may be designated 'go/no go' points, or gateways, where there is an opportunity to assess whether the project should continue, be substantially revised or abandoned. An example of a go/no go point might be the moment of sign-off following acceptance testing of software or following a pilot go-live to assess if further implementation can proceed. Staging of this kind can also assist in creating a more comfortable framework for the consideration of major changes. The establishment of planned times and methods for deciding whether particular designs work, and whether the benefits and costs are in the right balance, can make it easier for decision-makers to agree to proceed with projects, even though they have misgivings about some of the possibilities or find uncertainty difficult to manage. The inclusion of process evaluation in the project plan can be an essential aid in making 'go/no go' decisions, or passing gateway points.

In order to design a project in stages, key decision points and decision-makers need to be identified, along with specifying the criteria and information they will use. Important meetings need to be timed accordingly (while allowing for some slippage). In effect, each stage needs its own plan. While this may sound daunting, it can, in fact, make the task easier, because the planning is broken down into manageable pieces, and detailed planning for later stages can be deferred.

Budgeting

A budget is a financial document that projects income and expenses. It is a written forecast or plan of what managers expect to happen in the future, quantified in terms of dollar inflows (revenue) and dollar outflows (expenses) (Van Horne 1998). Organisations use budgets as planning tools to allocate resources and to evaluate their overall operations. For a project, the budget specifies all costs involved in completing the project and the funding or revenue required to cover the costs (when revenue and costs are equal, this is a 'balanced budget'). The fundamental purpose of the budget is to enable the project manager to track and measure actual results against the plan (Day et al. 2004). It provides important information to guide project monitoring and control, and indicates where action is required (to reduce overall expenses, or change practice and systems to reduce supply costs, and so on). A good budget is built on good estimation of time and costs, and on consideration of uncertainties and risks; and it makes adequate funds available for achievement of the project goals.

Budget development

The literature on project budget development and control (including Dobie 2007; Hill 2010; Kloppenborg 2009; PMI 2017, pp. 238-41; Roberts 2011) generally recommends that those preparing budgets undertake the following steps:

- Conduct a thorough analysis of the scope of work and tasks, activities and timelines, labour and other resources required to complete the work—the WBS provides a solid basis for completing this step.
- Assign realistic monetary values to the required resources, based on estimates for each item—thus forming a preliminary budget.
- Identify risk factors and allow for their potential impact on the budget—the risk management plan provides a good basis for calculating a contingency allowance for risk.
- Present and discuss the preliminary budget with senior management (and perhaps financial sponsors if relevant) to test that your thinking and calculations are in line with expectations, to explore the reasons for any differences and then resolve them.

In the implementation phase, the budget becomes the primary document for monitoring and controlling costs. The budget format depends largely on the project itself and on organisational systems and financial management practice, but a single spreadsheet can be used to list all project revenue and **expenditure items**. Expenditure items can be grouped according to type, for example **labour** (staff) or non-labour (equipment/materials) items, and fixed versus variable expenses. Budgets are normally '**cashflowed**' (that is, costs are allocated over the weeks or months of the project) so that expenditure can be monitored against time and linked to progress.

Identifying and estimating costs

Cost estimation is an unavoidable part of developing a budget. Project managers may be able to get valuable help from the organisation's finance staff, but those staff will need good instructions about what to include, and the expected size or volume of the resource (for example, programming time to capture the data from a new care process; duration of a group health education program; number of participants for a community activity; how many test kits for a new approach to monitoring a chronic disease; and so on). Essentially, the following resources in the project must be planned for, and their costs estimated:

- The staff (labour) required to do the work of the project, both within and outside the organisation. The time of the project manager and project team members, even if they are salaried staff, should be included, along with any additional expertise that may have to be 'purchased' in the form of legal advice, consultants, statisticians, agency staff and so on. Check your organisation's financial policies for the need to include labour 'on-costs' (typically up to 25 per cent on top of base-rate salaries, to cover the costs of superannuation, workers compensation insurance, leave entitlements, penalty rates and so on).
- Equipment, services and materials that will be needed for conducting the project—that is, the **direct costs** of setting up the project office, and all the consumables required.
- Specialised resources or products that need to be purchased as part of the deliverables (for example, hardware and software needed to implement a new patient management system, or access to a gym to trial a physical-activity program for people with a chronic condition).

As far as possible, costs should be based not on 'guesstimates' but on data gathered from the organisation's finance and payroll systems, together with prices from suppliers and quotations for any externally provided services or equipment. If the project will last for more than one year, costs should be indexed for inflation or salary increases (finance staff can advise on formulae for doing this).

Again, it is sometimes difficult for one person to come up with a comprehensive list, and team brainstorming and fact-checking is often the fastest way to develop a list and estimate the cost of each of item (Kovacevic et al. 2001; Lock 2007). Detailed estimating is often one of the first tasks challenging a newly appointed project manager. If a working group was formed at the project initiation phase, this group can contribute. Project managers can also seek input from others likely to be involved in the project, and from senior management and finance staff. For capital projects, independent cost consultants are usually required.

One way to check your list of expected cost items is to consider two categories: items that are unique to the project (these are more likely to be identified); and items that are necessary to the project but more routine—these are more likely to be forgotten, but finance staff or others with experience can help. Table 7.2 provides examples based on two projects.

Table 7.2 Examples of project cost items

Title: Hip fracture prevention project	Title: Androgenic anabolic steroids prevention project
Cost items unique to the project • Employment of a specialist nurse • Development of risk assessment manual **Cost items that may be common to all projects and easily forgotten** • Preparation for staff training and time for staff to attend • After-training follow-up • Supervision of implementation of risk assessments by staff • Survey on effectiveness of staff training workshop • Data collection and analysis, and report writing for the survey	**Cost items unique to the project** • Purchase of measurement instruments for appearance distress survey • Employment of a facilitator to conduct the workshops • Development and printing workshop materials **Cost items that may be common to all projects and easily forgotten** • Preparation of workshops • Workshop participants recruitment and selection • Input into appearance distress survey conduct and analysis by staff psychologist • Pre-post surveys on changes in knowledge and practice among participants as a result of the workshops • Data collection and analysis, and report writing for the survey

Other common cost items, such as supervision of the project leader, overhead costs, publicity (for both the project and staff recruitment) and promotion, may also be easily forgotten.

Project managers in health and community services often report difficulty with estimating staffing requirements, timelines and other costs correctly. Sometimes the budgeting requirement is skipped entirely for internal projects, and those responsible simply incorporate the project costs in their ongoing operational budgets. When this works, it is simple and perhaps more comfortable, but when it doesn't—for example, by causing unexpected and unexplained cost overruns—the consequences can be troublesome for the budget holders. It is a good idea to be clear about those costs that will be absorbed in operational budgets (with the agreement of the budget holder) and those that need to be included in the project budget.

Direct and indirect costs

Expenses or costs can be categorised as direct or indirect (Martin 2002; Courtney & Briggs 2004). Direct costs are incurred by and for the project—that is, they would not be incurred by the organisation otherwise. They may include the following:

- salaries, wages and other benefits (such as superannuation) for those working directly on the project, including the project leader, project officers and others who contribute (perhaps on a part-time or sessional basis) to getting the project done
- communication costs, such as project-specific telephone charges, printing and postage (such as a community mailout or the printing of special project stationery)
- transport and travel costs incurred by project staff specifically for project activities (such as taxis, flights or special courier services used by the project)
- equipment and computer software or hardware used solely for the project (such as tablets for participant voting in community meetings)
- project staff training and professional development
- consumables and stationery used in project activities (such as refreshments supplied to focus groups).

Indirect costs, often called 'overheads', are incurred for a common or joint purpose and therefore cannot be identified readily and attributed to a particular project. These costs may be necessary for the implementation and completion of the project, but are shared with other activities within the organisation. Project indirect costs may include:

- salaries, wages and other benefits for staff who don't work on the project, but who administer or otherwise support the project as part of their ongoing job, such as department administrator, ward clerk or IT staff
- general-purpose equipment, computers and software such as word processing programs

- space and utility costs
- general-purpose office supplies, such as paper, pens and toner cartridges
- routine internal courier services and general postage
- routine printing, reproduction and photocopying
- basic telephone and pager charges
- subscriptions, organisational memberships, practice books, and journal and magazine subscriptions used by the organisation
- insurance, such as public liability
- supervision of project leader.

In some circumstances, expenses normally charged as indirect costs may be charged to the project as direct costs. For example, large, complex projects that involve extensive data accumulation or surveying may need to employ an administration officer to support this work rather than using existing administrative staff—this would be a direct cost. Similarly, some overhead costs are routinely allocated to their end use, and if the project is included in this procedure (for example, a large or externally funded project may require a cost centre in its own right), these costs will be allocated as if they were direct.

Getting the budget right: not too little, not too much

The art of budgeting is to set the costs correctly, without either padding the budget through unrealistic assumptions (like zero delays in recruitment or allocation of staff) or, on the other hand, overlooking or underestimating significant cost items. Budgeting can be hard for many reasons, including that it may be a new role for project leaders/teams.

Health and community services face constant pressure to reduce costs without compromising service delivery. Projects are usually not immune from this pressure, so the principle of cost containment needs to be applied throughout the project planning process, including particularly in relation to salary costs, which are often the biggest single item.

The golden rule of budgeting

The 'golden rule' for developing a good budget is to ensure all items that are included in the budget are allocable, allowable, reasonable and necessary, and are being treated consistently (Dobie 2007; Martin 2002).

- A cost is *allocable* to a particular project when it can be directly attributed to it—that is, the cost really belongs to the project.

For example, a project leader purchases equipment to be used for work on a funded project. The equipment is allocable to the project as a direct cost. The project leader also purchases printer toner for his office printer, which is used for all of his unit activities. This is not directly attributable to any one project, and is therefore not allocable and may not be charged as a direct cost to the project. Instead, costs of using the printer for project work can be allocated to the project on the basis of either an actual usage charge (such as using a project pass code for the printer) or a rule of thumb (for example, 20 per cent of the printing for this month is for the project).

- Only costs allowed by the organisation's policy, or accepted as common practice, can be included. For example, a project leader has a project officer working on the project. This is an *allowable* direct cost of the project. However, the project leader may consider discussing the project with the project officer over dinner. If meal expenses are not allowed by the organisation's policy, this is not an allowable cost and may not be built into the project budget.

- A cost must be *reasonable* and *necessary* for the performance of the project. For example, a project leader purchases lab supplies to be used for the project. The supplies are reasonable and necessary for the project and may be charged to the project as direct costs. At the same time, the project leader considers purchasing a car, as a lot of local travelling will be required during the project. This is not reasonable or necessary, as it is more efficient to hire a car or reimburse staff for use of their own vehicles, or use public transport.

- Costs incurred for the same purpose in like circumstances within the organisation must be *treated consistently* as either direct or indirect costs. That is, if the organisation generally treats a particular type of cost as direct (and therefore allocable), the same cost can't be treated as indirect anywhere within the organisation. The reason for this rule is to avoid incorrect or double charging. Similarly, current practice should be used as the guide when deciding how to name and categorise each budget item, for consistency in accounting treatment. That is, if lab supplies (for example) are to be used in the project, they should be categorised in the same way as they would be in normal use.

Budget items

The project budget should be developed to include all predicted expenses that will be incurred during the whole project period—and all relevant income that will cover predicted expenses. In principle, project expenses and income (which may be allocated from internal sources) should be equal, to ensure that the project can be financially self-sufficient. A budget usually includes five categories in the expense section as detailed in Table 7.3. However, the grouping of budget items can be different between organisations depending on their accounting practice. For example, budget items can also be grouped as fixed, variable and semi-fixed costs. Finance staff can be very helpful with getting the categories and grouping right. They are also more likely to support the project manager with budget problems during the project if they understand the budgeting decisions and if the budget has been correctly structured and documented.

Sources of funding and other resources

In health and community services, the resources needed for the project may be acquired from four major sources:

1. external funding (from government and non-government sources)
2. internal allocation of funds (such as from fee-for-service activities or interest earned)
3. **'in-kind' funding** (resources but not cash). This can be either internal (such as staff time, office space or administrative support), or external (such as access to meeting rooms in the local hospital for a medication management workshop being run by the community health service)
4. donations.

Each funding source brings obligations and expectations, from formal funding contract obligations to government funders, to expectations for acknowledgement and appreciation (for example, if the organisation's volunteer or fundraising group funds the project).

There may also be resources that are readily accessible to the project without cost or obligation. In the case of a project aiming at improving medication management skills of people with high blood pressure, brochures may be freely available to the project from the local health department. These contributions should be included in the detailed

Table 7.3 Budget categories and items

Budget categories	Items
Labour costs (staffing)	• Salaries • Consultancies • Agency costs • Oncosts: superannuation, recreation leave, sick leave, possibly workers compensation insurance, allowances etc.
Administrative costs	• Staff supervision • Financial management • Administrative support
Operational costs	• Postage • Stationery • Meeting costs (venue hire, catering etc.) • Office space/rental • Travelling expenses • Telephone/fax/mobile/internet • Advertising and marketing costs • Printing and promotional materials • Staff training and development • Contractor costs (e.g. design of evaluation survey or evaluation contract)
Capital costs (major asset purchase)	• Equipment • Office furnishing • Office building or vehicles (very unlikely for projects) • Software • Vendor/contractor costs
Other items	• Necessary items specific to the project and not included above

budget on the 'revenue' side, even when the dollar value is zero, in the 'in-kind' category. This not only makes it clear to funders that all available resources have been marshalled by the project (something they generally appreciate), but can also be useful for future planning for projects and ongoing services.

Projects are often used to pilot new ways of providing services or managing operations, and a full record of all resources required for a successful trial provides an important input to decision-making about ongoing implementation of the project outcomes (for example, by routinely offering a new service or doing business in the new way). It can also be helpful to be able to show funders, key stakeholders and sponsors that the project has attracted more resources than the ones they are being asked to fund or otherwise support.

Constructing a detailed budget

If a work breakdown structure has been prepared, the details of work packages provide the basis for writing a detailed budget. The activities and tasks are already specified, and it is then more straightforward to identify the resources required and estimate their costs. For example, if a nurse with expertise in high blood pressure education is needed for workshops in medication management, the first step is to find out what classification or salary level should be offered for this nurse specialist (based on education and experience requirements). The next steps will be to calculate how many days or hours of time are needed per week or per workshop for all required tasks (such as preparation of workshop materials and data recording), and for how long (how many weeks or workshops).

Once all required resources for each work package have been listed, they can be entered into the budget template. A good budget template will remind you of what may have been left out.

For a project where a WBS may not be justified, or may not yet have been completed, a good estimation of project costs can be prepared by listing all the essential tasks and the resources and time required to complete them, and then calculating their costs. There are many templates for developing a full project budget, and the organisation may well require a certain format (which can be modified if necessary for the special requirements of the project). Table 7.4 is an example of a budget that has been developed for the androgenic anabolic steroids prevention project.

Budgeting for contingencies

When the budget is taking shape, it is helpful for the project manager and working group to make time to reflect on the uncertainties in the project itself that could affect the budget. The risk management plan (see Chapter 5), along with the budget document, provide the starting point. The source of funding for the project, for example government funding, may also determine the level or percentage of contingency that can be built into the business case.

Table 7.4 Project budget example

Resource (itemised)	Funds sought from Dept. of Health		In-kind donation from CHS	
	Year 1	Year 2	Year 1	Year 2
Staffing				
Project team leader 0.4 FTE (Health Service Manager Award Level 2 Year 1)	$38,199	$39,727		
Project officer 0.5 FTE (SACS Award Youth Worker C IV Year 1)	$26,580	$27,644		
School teachers 600 hours (State School Teacher Award Step 8)			$9,198	$9,567
Administration support 5 hrs/w (SACS Vic Award Class II Year 2)	$6,111	$6,355		
Total staff on-cost (23.5%)	$16,659	$17,325	$2,162	$2,248
Staff training and skills development				
Three days' group facilitation training for project officer	$1,271			
Half-day team-building training for project manager	$303			
Drug and Alcohol Prevention Conference in Victoria registration	$787			
Administrative costs				
Project team supervision from Director of Youth Programs (5 hrs/month, $69/hr including on-cost, 4% increase for year 2)	$4,138	$4,304		
*Insurance & financial management (5% of total program costs)	$9,854	$9,100		
Operational costs				
Office rental ($85/w, 4% increase for year 2)			$4,862	$5,057

Resource (itemised)	Funds sought from Dept. of Health		In-kind donation from CHS	
	Year 1	Year 2	Year 1	Year 2
Telephone/fax/mobile cost (2 mobile $60/m + $60/m landline)	$2,160	$2,471		
Printing & postage for letters to parents ($0.75 x 800 per year)	$600	$624		
Stationery and other printing ($165/m)	$1,980	$2,059		
Measurement instrument for survey	$1,650			
Recruitment costs e.g. project staff & facilitators	$2,904			
Tea, coffee for student workshops ($8/person x 600 students x 5 sessions per year)	$24,000	$24,960		
Tea, coffee & lunch for three days' intensive training for health professionals ($27.5/person x 3 days x 120 people)	$9,900			
Venue for health-staff training: $380/day x 3 days x 4 series)			$4,560	
Venue for student workshops ($130 x 5 sessions x 20 series per year)			$13,000	$13,520
Travelling expenses (local travel to meetings, schools and workshops (35 km x 164 travels x $0.68/km)	$3,903	$4,072		
Capital costs				
Laptop computer with software	$2,530	-		-
Desktop computer with software			$1,980	
Office furnishing			$715	
Fax machines			$385	
Two telephone sets	$605			

Table 7.4 Project budget example *continued*

Resource (itemised)	Funds sought from Dept. of Health		In-kind donation from CHS	
	Year 1	Year 2	Year 1	Year 2
Data projector (rental) ($244/w for 4 weeks each year)	$962	$962		
Promotional costs				
Poster and brochure design	$1,513			
Printing poster ($28 x 120)	$3,360			
Printing of brochures ($0.55 x 1500)	$825			
Printing of training materials for health professionals ($30 x 120)	$3,600			
Printing of information for parents ($0.55 x 600)	$330	$363		
Printing of handout for students at the workshops ($3 x 600 per year)	$1,800	$1,980		
Evaluation costs				
**Internal evaluation cost (2% of total project cost)		$7,961		
External evaluation consultant ($190/hr x 76 hrs)		$14,440		
Total cost	**$166,524**	**$164,347**	**$36,862**	**$30,392**
Total cost including 10% GST	**$183,176**	**$180,782**	**$40,548**	**$33,431**
Total funds being sought from DoH		**$363,958**		
Total donation in-kind		**$73,979**		
Total Budget		**$437,937**		

*Calculation of 5% insurance & financial management: 5% of total cost of the individual year expenses, including funding being sought and donation in-kind (excluding evaluation cost)

**Calculation of 2% internal evaluation cost: 2% of total cost of all expenses for the whole project (both years), including funding being sought and donation in-kind

To identify the need for a contingency budget, the following questions might be relevant:

- Does the budget include any identified contingency funds, or estimates that already allow for potential contingencies?
- Are there any special expectations by senior management or the funder that have cost implications?
- Is there professional expertise within the organisation that the project can utilise?
- Is there any professional expertise that is critical to the project and may be hard to find? If so, what are the implications?
- Are there any expected difficulties in recruiting staff? Can any existing staff be allocated to the project?
- Have evaluation costs (based on the evaluation plan and funder requirements) been included?

Answers to the above questions may have different but significant effects on the project budget. For example, if difficulties in staff recruitment are expected or internal recruitment of staff is impossible, staff recruitment costs need to be included in the project budget. The impact of delay in staff recruitment on the project costs, and perhaps on its timing, should be factored in. Sometimes a potential project is just too complex to estimate with confidence—and perhaps too complex for the organisation to conduct. Scaling it down, or restricting the project to just a first stage, might be necessary.

The project business case

In project management, a business case is essentially a project plan and financial analysis that quantifies and schedules the costs of a project as well as the benefits and direct cost savings or increased revenue arising from the project. A positive business case is one in which the benefits (which normally arise after the project is completed) outweigh the costs. The origin of the term lies in the small business field, where typically an owner of a small business (or intending owner of one) needs to present a positive business case to their bank or potential investors in order to get the capital needed to open or extend the business—that is, it is essentially a plan that demonstrates that the business is capable of repaying the investor or financier. Preparing a business plan can be important for small business owners for other reasons, as it essentially forces the owner to answer the question: 'How can this business be profitable?'

The concept of a positive business case is a bit different for projects in health and community services. The question may instead be 'will this project enable us to do something differently or better without additional cost—can we make this pay for itself?' (the 'break even' argument). For private providers of services, the question may be 'can we make this pay for itself and generate at least an acceptable surplus?'.

If there are potential returns if a project works, but its costs are significant and sources of funding are hard to find, a well-argued business case can give decision-makers a compelling reason to find the money and make the investment (Dobie 2007). In some situations, a signed-off business case may be required to get a mandate for the project. In addition to showing how innovative and effective the proposed project could be, the business case needs to address how the proposed project can justify the resources required (or how implementation of its outcomes will be sustainable); how it will contribute to the achievement of the organisation's and/or funder's strategic goals; and, if possible, how it will complement or enhance other approved initiatives and thus maximise their benefits. However, the business case does not need to be complicated.

Writing a business case

The business case document will be used as a tool for raising interest among key stakeholders and potential funders. It should address the following questions:

- What strategic benefits will the project bring to the organisation?
- Why is the project good value for money, given that the organisation will make a considerable investment in the project?
- What are the consequences for the organisation if it were not to conduct this project?
- What is the evidence that supports the case (in a form that is useful for decision-makers)?
- On what criteria will success of the project (and a decision to proceed with implementation of the result) be based?

All of the detailed planning and budgeting work will provide much of the information needed for the writing of a business case. The business case should be as concise and clear as possible, while including all necessary practical details. There are plenty of business case templates available (for example, www.projectmanagementdocs.com/template/Business-Case-Template.doc), and Table 7.5 provides a generic business case outline for consideration.

Table 7.5 Generic business case outline

Executive summary	A concise summary (ideally on two pages) of the content of the document, including all recommendations. It should read as a 'standalone' document, and should not introduce any material not found in the body of the report.
Sign-off sheet	An endorsement clause for recording project sponsors' and proponents' signatures, either committing them to act on the business case, or recording their support.
Current situation	A statement of the background and current context with relevant facts and judgements backed up with evidence (expressed in numbers where possible).
Future state	The intended, predicted or desired future situation or environment. That is, the realisation of goals and strategies, the future role delineation, risk profile and service models etc. Any assumptions should be clearly set out and supported with relevant data or other evidence.
Policy issues	The broad policy, political, legislative and organisational constraints within which the business case must fit. For example, government goals and policies, social justice considerations, legislative requirements, accreditation and strategic directions.
Strategic alignment	How does the initiative align with the organisation's or funder's strategic goals?
Gap/needs analysis	A statement of the problems, gaps or needs that the project seeks to address, supported with relevant data and analysis.
Options for action	All feasible options to address the problems or gaps within the policy constraints. Each option, including the 'base case' or 'do nothing' option, should be described in enough detail to establish workable alternative courses of action. Each option must be capable of standing alone.
Analysis of options	The analysis of options is both a qualitative and quantitative process. Typical components include: income and expenditure streams; sources of funds for capital and recurrent costs; economic analyses (such as cost utility); NPV (Net Present Value) tables; risk analysis; volume of outputs or services; strategic considerations; and timing. The analysis of each facet should conclude with a definitive result or solution, since these results will be used for comparison between options, and selection of a preferred option.

Table 7.5 Generic business case outline *continued*

Comparative evaluation and selection of preferred option	Based on the results of the steps above and a clear statement of argument, the criteria and process, the preferred option is identified (this explanation usually also appears in the executive summary).
Recommendations	Recommendations propose the preferred option in the form of a decision or action for decision-makers to endorse or decline. Any needed information about decision-making processes and the management of differing perceptions or other issues in the approval process should be included.
Implementation plan	Specifies the team or individual responsible for implementation, and outlines the main components of the project plan.
Appendices	Additional material used and referred to in the business case. For example, members of the project team, additional financial or service data and analysis, population profile or other demographic data, equipment lists and references.

What about projects with no positive business case?

For some projects, there is no way that the project results can be applied without additional costs—for example, the introduction of a new keyhole surgical technique will probably expand the number of patients who can be treated and therefore cost a public hospital or health authority more, even if the procedure itself is more efficient. A new diversion program for young people at risk of offending will probably bring no financial benefit or reduced costs or 'offsets' to the provider of the program—cost savings will be realised in other agencies, such as juvenile detention facilities. In this sort of case, the question may be 'can we justify this additional service to funders on the basis of health or welfare benefits, and thus savings to the broader service system?'. This is essentially the argument that health or social harms will be prevented and money will be saved elsewhere in the health or welfare system— even if there are extra costs for the organisation that provides the service. If this is the basis on which justification will rest, an economic analysis may be what is needed (see Chapter 6). The results of a needs analysis or other empirical evidence can also be useful, as illustrated in Case 7.1.

Case 7.1 Positive health outcomes: negative business case

A Primary Health Network had identified that people with chronic diseases in their region were experiencing higher than average hospital admission rates. A check of compliance with clinical guidelines for chronic condition management in primary care by GPs and other local practitioners revealed that standards were being met and in some cases exceeded, so they needed to look elsewhere. There is evidence to suggest that patients and carers are particularly open to changing their practices at home immediately following a crisis that leads to admission, so the local hospital was a logical place to look.

The Network approached the local hospital with proposals for improvements in the way the hospital assisted patients and carers to prepare for improved management of chronic conditions following discharge. The hospital quickly realised that engaging in the suggested changes in their practices would cost real money during the pre-discharge period (e.g. building in training and time for senior clinical nurses and junior doctors to provide direct coaching to patients and families), but that the benefits of improved effectiveness would not flow to savings for the hospital. If the suggested measures worked, patients' wellbeing would benefit, and possibly their future disease course would change. However, the hospital did not have the capacity in its budget to fund the initiative, and there was simply no workable business case. They agreed with the PHN to work on a submission for research or philanthropic funding to test the effectiveness of the measures, and thus prove the health benefits and net cost savings to the local health system.

Summary

- The work breakdown structure (WBS) is useful for estimating the time and resources required for the project.
- WBS enables sequencing of project tasks, and estimation of their duration. It also allows the identification of time and resource issues in the project planning phase.
- Estimation of time and costs is important to good project planning. However, estimation is never perfect for something that has never been done before. A number of strategies can be adopted to improve the quality of estimation.
- A budget is an important document to plan income and expenses for the project, and provides project managers with the ability to measure actual results against planned expectations.
- Budgets should be based on experience, good understanding of the project and its tasks, and team effort. Budget development should be guided by the important features of costs—budget items should be allocable, allowable, reasonable and necessary, and be treated consistently.
- A business case can assist in clarifying the importance or priority of a proposed project, and will help decision-makers to understand the value of the project, leading to their support.

Readings and resources

Templates:

Project Business case template: www.projectmanagementdocs.com/templates/business-case-template.html

Project Development and Reporting (including Budget template): www.aciar.gov.au/Our-Research/Project-Development-and-Reporting

Readings:

Hill, G.M., 2009, *The Complete Project Management Methodology and Toolkit*, Roca Raton: CRC Press.

Roberts, P., 2011, *Effective Project Management*, London: Kogan Page.

Victor A., Bañuls V.A., López C., Turoff M. & Tejedor F., 2017, 'Predicting the impact of multiple risks on project performance: A scenario-based approach', *Project Management Journal*, vol. 48, no. 5, pp. 95–114.

8

The implementation phase I: making it happen

The implementation (or execution) phase is the time when plans become reality and strategies are implemented. The project manager's focus shifts to two key goals: making the project happen (the focus of this chapter), and controlling and completing the project (the focus of Chapter 9).

In this chapter, we first discuss the management and leadership tasks of this phase, and the challenges of achieving change in the project, including some brief explanation of theories about change. We suggest some methods for making sustainable change happen, and for dealing with the project politics and resistance to change.

Getting started

Implementation of a project is about leading and motivating people, together with coordinating human and other resources to carry out the plan.

The processes of making the project happen can be described as:

- project plan execution—performing the activities on the plan
- team development—developing individual and group skills/ competencies to enhance project performance
- communication and information distribution—making needed information available to project stakeholders in a timely manner
- stakeholder management—working with stakeholders as the project unfolds, shoring up their commitment, responding to their concerns and monitoring any shifting alliances
- change management—attending to the challenges of change that the project brings for staff and the organisation.

The sum total of these activities can be overwhelming for the project manager. So where do you start? The project plan is the key, and this is when the benefits of planning are realised.

Where the project manager has been appointed after the development of the plan, a review of the plan and any associated business case is a good place to start. Is the plan realistic? Are there any glaring omissions? Was some of the planning not detailed enough? Have project activities commenced already? If there are problems with the plan at the commencement of the project implementation, now is the time to address them—the sooner the better.

For the project manager new to the project and/or the organisation or unit in which the project sits, the first step is to understand the project's history and the context. Finding out the background to the project, how it developed and who was involved can assist further on if the project seems to hit brick walls, is being 'white-anted', or when something is happening that you just cannot put your finger on.

As the project is getting started, it's often a good idea to think about potential risks and sticking points that are likely to arise and how they could be resolved. This requires careful listening, honest thinking and informed logical analysis. It can be helpful to stand back from daily concerns and really analyse what's going on around the project and where the problems are likely to come from. One method is to tell yourself the story of how this project succeeds: what are the key mysteries that are solved and the turning points that will make the difference? This technique can be used to identify the negatives as well: if this project were to fail, what would the causes be and who would be the villains of the story? These techniques are a kind of rehearsal for managing and leading the project, and can be used in preparation for important presentations or meetings as well.

Leadership, motivation and teamwork

> Projects depend on relationships.
>
> *(Berkun 2018)*

Leadership, particularly for motivation and good teamwork (working together to a common purpose or shared goal) is essential in creating successful project outcomes. The guidelines in the following list can help project managers to achieve these objectives:

- Do not lose sight of the goal of the project—whatever strategies you develop, they must be focused on achieving this goal.
- Timelines are important—while some flexibility might be necessary, too much flexibility will see you lose control of the project.
- Problems and potential problems must be identified and dealt with—they are unlikely to just go away, and might get bigger and come back to bite you at the most inconvenient time.
- Attention to detail is essential—it can help you identify problems and keep your eye on emerging issues, so keep good notes and records.

- Keep your eye on the ball—work the project; it will not happen by itself.
- Walk your talk—make sure that you do what you say you will do; model good project management practice.
- Hone your communication skills—be a good listener and approachable; provide clear, easy-to-read written reports and memos that are short and to the point.
- Improve your facilitation skills, especially in meetings—make all meetings productive, or people will stop attending.
- Recognise the skills and work of others, and give praise where appropriate—give credit where credit is due, but also deal with non-performance.
- Take responsibility—beware of blaming others for problems.
- Encourage good working relationships—through good humour, a positive attitude and a 'we can do this' approach.
- Aim to be someone who creates and gives out good energy—rather than a black hole that sucks the energy out of others.

Action learning

One of the more challenging leadership tasks is ensuring that the project team 'rolls with the punches' and is constantly assessing and refining the evolving project's methods and focus. Action learning (or the related idea of reflexive practice) is an approach that may be useful for this task. Action learning is the practice of thoughtful consideration (and discussion) of events, a process by which people make sense of their experience and its meaning (DeFillippi 2001; Gleeson et al. 2016; Leggat et al. 2011).

Project managers can promote action learning in their teams by the simple method of encouraging thoughtful discussion and analysis of any aspect of a project that seems either troublesome or potentially rewarding, or that might be seen as a 'critical incident' (for example, a walkout by a stakeholder). Regular team meetings can be used both to address normal project business and to encourage reflection and learning. The major challenge with this technique is to establish an environment of trust and safety so that team members can engage in open, thoughtful discussion, and then to maintain a climate of safety through mutual commitment to confidentiality and constructive use of discussion outcomes. At the commencement of the project and when the team is established, it may be useful to conduct a project induction and orientation process where the project 'code of conduct' can be discussed.

Establishing the project team

Recruiting a project team can be a challenging and fraught process, sometimes undertaken in the rush to commence the implementation phase of the project. Determining who will be part of the team often happens during the initiation and planning phases. The recruitment process may be formal or informal and will depend partly on whether recruitment is internal, external or a mixture of both. If external, the formal recruitment process will include internal approvals, advertising, shortlisting, interviews, letter of offer and contract; or engaging with a contractor to provide specified services. The process may be informal when organisational rules allow and leaders prefer.

Internal recruitment involves the secondment (or release) of staff to the project team. This may be a formal process of advertising project positions internally, then interviewing, followed by selection and appointment; or people may be identified and approached by the project sponsor or manager—and some negotiation with their usual line manager will probably be needed. Internal recruitment can be a sensitive and emotionally charged process, with line managers sometimes perceiving that they are losing quality staff to the project with negative effect on their department. The availability of funding to support backfill, so that the staff member's normal work can continue, might also be a critical consideration. It is important to be flexible, communicate well and negotiate with managers regarding the terms of the secondment, lead times, commencement dates and duration, availability of backfill funding, dual reporting and how the process of transition at both ends of the project will work.

Tips for effective project team recruitment:
- Clarify expectations regarding formality of recruitment processes required for your project from an organisational, human resources and industrial relations perspective.
- Clarify the requirements and attributes of the role, including qualifications, skills, award classification, salary range and conditions.
- Develop position descriptions for each project team role and ensure that the sponsor or steering committee approves them.

- Use an open recruitment process (including advertising the project team positions and conducting interviews) if possible, both for getting the best people and for satisfying general staff expectations of fairness and opportunity. But circumstances or organisational culture might not support this.
- Involve the key stakeholders, and clarify your authority in the decision-making regarding project team appointments.
- Communicate effectively and often with all the stakeholders, in particular the managers to whom the staff report.
- Be familiar with the policies and processes for effectively transitioning staff onto the project team, including employee contracts, credentialling, variation of employment forms, timesheets, rostering systems, budgeting and cost-centre management.

Managing project staff

Building a project team that works well together is a key part of project success. All the normal requirements of good people management and effective teamwork apply. Good management of a project team also requires effective responses to three important issues:

1. the problem of two bosses
2. the challenge of rapid skills development
3. the question of retention of a temporary team until their work is really done.

Some team members will probably only report to the project manager for the duration of the project, or may continue to be supervised by their normal line manager throughout. Openness between the two managers involved can help avoid a situation where the team member feels pulled in two directions. A clear delineation of the split in reporting relationships is essential. For example: Who approves leave? Who does performance appraisal? Who can make demands on the person's time and for what? How will the managers keep each other informed in a way that is fair to the staff member?

In many cases, team members may have only some of the skills the project needs. Although the project cannot wait for long-term skill development, all team members need to be confident in the specific methods and tools that will be used in this project. It is therefore usually a good idea to hold training workshop/s for the team to explain and finalise the project's chosen methods, tools, templates and reports, and to train team members in their use. Topics such as running effective meetings, process mapping techniques and interviewing skills could also be covered. Competence can improve rapidly when some training (and opportunity to ask questions) is provided; when tools and templates are used consistently across the team; and when team members are able to use the project manager and other leaders as models. Staff should be given the opportunity to identify their areas of interest and strength as well as those areas where they lack skills or confidence. Then either their roles can be structured accordingly, or further skills training can be arranged.

Finally, towards the end of the project, there can be a tendency for team members (and maybe the manager) to focus on returning to their units or seeking further project opportunities, rather than on finishing the project. It is a good idea to raise this issue at the beginning and work out strategies for meeting both the needs of the team members and the needs of the project.

At the least, the manager, and maybe one or two others, could be contracted until well after the expected completion date to allow for slippage and for project closing and bedding-down activities. This will give them a period after the project is practically completed to focus on their next moves. Team members and the project manager could also negotiate agreements with the operational manager to cover problems with timing or any other aspect of the return to the operational area, and agree on a process to be followed if these contingencies arise.

Early attention to these important issues, and establishing an environment of safety and clear expectations among the project team, will pay off in enhanced capacity to deliver results—and weather storms—as the project progresses.

Problem-solving skills

During the course of the project, it might become obvious that the project team has gaps in its skills and knowledge, or conflicts might emerge between team members or other groups and individuals. This can be one of the most challenging things that a manager has to deal with, inside or outside a project. While there are many techniques and methods for dealing with conflict, basic problem-solving skills are particularly relevant.

It is important to keep an open mind in order to recognise problems as they begin to emerge in the project team. We suggest the following problem–solving process:

- Accept that a problem exists, and resolve to take action.
- Dispassionately gather the facts.
- Define the problem.
- Understand what is causing the problem.
- Engage the team in contributing to both understanding the problem and finding solutions.
- Agree to the solution.
- Plan the response and implement it.

The GRPI framework (goals, roles, processes and interpersonals) is an effective tool both for promoting good teamwork and for analysing and addressing team problems (Johnson 2010). It is sometimes drawn as an inverted pyramid, to make it clear that shared goals are the starting point (the biggest element) for good teams. The other elements are clearly defined roles for team members (no gaps or unhelpful overlaps); reliable processes and systems (that enable people to get their jobs done); and, only then, interpersonal factors. That is, poor team functioning may appear to be caused by interpersonal problems, and that is often where the pain is felt, but the source of the problem probably lies elsewhere, and the manager needs to pay attention to factors higher up the order. Figure 8.1 illustrates this model.

Figure 8.1 The GRPI framework

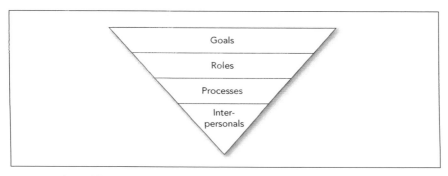

Source: Adapted from Rubin et al. 1977

Conducting effective meetings

Project meetings fulfil many important functions in most projects, and are necessary for effective communication. They will be more effective if they are properly scheduled, have a well-structured agenda, and are briefly recorded in minutes that include required action and reporting. There will be different types of meetings with different people participating—project team, steering committee, executive briefings, vendor meetings, stakeholder meetings—which will probably require various approaches to decision-making, structuring the agenda, facilitating discussion and reporting progress and outcomes.

Good meeting and facilitation skills can help to save time, diffuse conflict and make things happen. There are two underlying principles in facilitation. The first is the need to be efficient: people are busy and don't want to waste valuable time in unproductive meetings. Being clear about the purpose of each agenda item, and what the meeting needs to achieve to progress it, will help everyone keep on topic. The second is participation: people need to have their voices heard and feel that they are contributing if they are to have some ownership of the project and maintain their commitment. We suggest the following guidelines for good meeting facilitation:

- Always have an agenda—no matter how small and informal the meeting.
- Know the meeting timelines and stick to them—start on time (habitual latecomers will probably get the message), put time limits against agenda items and stick to them unless there is a very good reason not to.
- The facilitator does not have to know the answer to every question—put difficult points back to the meeting or agree how they will be 'parked' and dealt with later.
- Keep things moving along—do not let participants ramble.
- Encourage some people to speak.
- Be prepared to shut others up—nicely!
- Keep on track—don't be taken off into irrelevant issues.
- Look for answers to difficult problems.
- Make sure every issue has an action—even if it is just 'defer to next meeting'.
- Make sure each action has an owner who is responsible for making it happen.
- Keep notes or minutes.

- Make sure you revisit minutes before the next meeting and deal with any matters arising.
- Keep a record of attendance.

Achieving sustainable change

We turn now to what is often the major implementation challenge the project team will face—achieving change through the project. Projects can be the biggest single enablers of changing the way organisations do things, by bringing the right people together to work towards important project goals.

Usually the whole purpose of a project is to bring in something new or to do something differently—that is, to innovate. Innovation is defined as the successful implementation of something new or, more simply, as 'putting ideas to work' (Department of Industry, Science and Resources 1999, p. 9). In health and community services, as in other spheres, innovation happens when a new process or system is introduced, even if the agency is not the first in the world to undertake that particular change.

During the implementation phase, the change management strategies outlined in the project plan for identifying, quantifying and managing the organisational impact of the project will be enacted. These activities may include change impact statements, change readiness assessment, business process review and policy review, as well as communication and training. As noted in Chapter 6, change is an ongoing process, and the change strategies identified in the project or change management plan will require monitoring and review throughout the implementation phase—are the strategies working? It may be that, despite enacting all the planned change strategies, a key stakeholder or group is persistently resistant, or a change readiness assessment shows that the organisation is NOT ready for the change (or go-live) to proceed.

Change fatigue is also commonly reported by staff in health services and organisations due to the constant, concurrent and often competing changes, and the magnitude of broader changes in the health sector. Organisational change fatigue is defined as a general sense of apathy or passive resignation towards organisational changes by individuals or teams (Wikipedia 2018a). It can threaten the success of change management efforts and the project itself. New strategies to counteract or avoid change fatigue may need to be considered by both the project and the organisation, such as prioritising one project (or change initiative) over others, providing backfill to attend training, providing additional support during the go-live period, or quarantining staff to enable them to only focus on one change initiative at a time.

In the following section, we focus on projects that need to achieve sustainable change in some aspect of the existing work system, power structure, working relationships, roles or responsibilities of people and teams—that is, where the change will affect people and their work. A lot has been written about achieving change in organisations, and much of it applies to projects. We briefly review some of the major theories and approaches to change that are relevant to project management and the politics of change, and then address the ways people respond to change, particularly when there is resistance.

Participative approaches to implementing change

The organisational change theorists tell us that while directive processes can achieve change quickly, it is the more participative approaches to change that create a sense of ownership and involvement among the major players (Stace & Dunphy 2001). The main critiques of participative change processes such as 'organisational development' are the slow pace of change (which is usually achieved in small, incremental steps), failure to deal with the difficulties of participation, and lack of acknowledgement of issues of power.

The change that is part of the project is proactive change, even when the project may have originated as a response to an external event or crisis. Projects are also generally aimed at sustainable change—that is, making sure that something not only changes in the short term but also becomes embedded in organisational practice. Both these characteristics tend to argue for a well-structured participative approach.

In a foundational study, McElroy (1996) articulates a clear argument in favour of the use of projects for achieving organisational change. He contrasts four methods of implementing change:

1. Education and communication—persuading staff of the need
2. Participation—staff assist management to define the change and the change process.
3. Intervention—management defines the required outcomes but uses projects to enable participation in the process.
4. Edict—where management gives precise instructions to be followed.

He concludes that intervention is the most effective. In this method, leaders make strategic decisions and set the parameters, using project methods to engage affected staff in designing and implementing operational change accordingly. The project approach is recommended because it enables the setting of clear goals and scope, and ensures they are authorised before the project begins. That is, management (in signing off on the project charter and plan) accepts its responsibility to resolve the question of 'should we seriously try this?' up front, before the work commences. While there are no guarantees, this method helps project teams and sponsors to handle the natural resistance from those who are affected, and to hold stakeholders to the project mandate.

Managing participation

While participatory approaches to change are useful, it is important to avoid 'death by process': endless meetings, surveys, workshops and interim reports that waste time, cause the project to lose momentum and reduce good will. The challenge is to balance openness, transparency and consultation with maintaining momentum and sticking to the project's goals and scope.

There are two main levels to managing participation. One is the project's leadership structure, including the engagement of stakeholders in committees (see below). The second is broader participation by staff generally and by members of stakeholder groups. The key to success with these methods is structured participation, with well-designed processes that ask the right questions at the right stage, and recognise that people want to have their say but are also busy. The givens—what is not negotiable—should be explicit, such as decisions already made by the executive or board, or the implications of government policy or legislation, to provide a framework around the areas of discretion.

Depending upon the project, stakeholder and context, the following methods may encourage participation:

- confidential one-to-one or small group discussions with project staff or others who are trusted by the group
- in discussions with affected staff (where their views will influence a decision), straw polls using computer-based 'voting' or its low-technology equivalents such as Post-it notes or dots on wall posters can accurately capture the majority view
- consultation with an independent expert may promote acceptance by a conflicted group.

The general principle is to use appropriate methods to gather meaningful results with an explicit method of analysing and using the outcomes. Most importantly, there needs to be a method of closing off the participation exercise and moving on.

The politics of change: managing the shadow side

One of the reasons that many change processes fail is that the proponents do not understand the politics of change. The health and community services sector comprises many powerful stakeholders who do not always have the same interests and often compete with each other for power and prestige. Organisations must manage tensions between providing a service and balancing a budget, between their espoused policy and their actual practice, between centralism and localism, between professionals and managers, and between innovation and tradition and comfort.

While some elements of the power structure (such as formal hierarchies, controls and resource allocation) are overt, much of the politics of the organisation, and of the project, happens in what Egan (1994) calls the 'shadow side'. According to Egan (1994, p. 41) the shadow side is:

> all the important activities and arrangements that do not get identified, discussed, and managed in decision-making forums that can make a difference. The shadow side deals with the covert, the undiscussed, the undiscussable and the unmentionable. It includes arrangements not found in organizational manuals and company documents or on organizational charts.

The shadow side, or the shadow system (Stacey 2001) is outside ordinary managerial intervention and can substantially affect productivity and the quality of working life, both positively and negatively. Much of what constitutes a supportive organisational culture are powerful positive elements of the shadow side. Other positive aspects include informal advocacy on behalf of the organisation, which many staff undertake both within and outside of work settings, and informal networks of communication that flow under and around formal channels and help both managers and staff know what is going on.

Negative elements can include:

- entrenched enmity between functional managers (affecting the ability of their departments to work together)

- a culture that accepts poor performance by favoured individuals
- executive or board members influenced in their decision-making by loyalty to an outside force (such as their professional association or their family's interests) rather than the organisation
- approvals processes that are not understood and documented
- manipulation of meeting agendas and minutes (matters not discussed at all, or discussion not minuted accurately).

There will always be a shadow side, and organisations will always have politics. The question is not whether, but to what extent and in what directions (helpful or harmful) do organisational politics operate? Good management, tolerance of difference and debate, and open communication will tend to minimise the space that the shadow side has to work in. That is, bringing important issues into the open and dealing with them in a careful way will reduce the need for negative shadow-side activity. Projects can be an opportunity to shine the spotlight on forgotten cupboards and remote attics in the organisation, and to deal constructively with shadow-side issues (but judgement is needed to decide which doors to open when).

Project managers by and large do not have a strong or stable power base (Pinto 2000), and learn to cultivate influence instead. The need for influence is made stronger by the fact that projects often exist outside the formal structures, and so all resources must be negotiated and bargained for. Lack of authority—for example, to conduct a performance review of project team members—also limits power, and project managers may even be managing their peers or their superiors. They have little managerial control in this situation, and so human skills become very important.

This has many implications for project politics. The first is that project managers must understand and acknowledge the political nature of most organisations, especially the influence of key stakeholders. The second is that project managers must learn to cultivate 'appropriate' political tactics.

One important tactic is to use the 'WIIFM'—what's in it for me?—principle. For example, departmental or unit loyalties and interests are usually more immediate and more powerful for most people than commitment to organisation-wide concerns, especially in large organisations. It can therefore be helpful to analyse proposals and issues in the project from the point of view of each of the departments or groups whose contribution, or acquiescence, is needed. When people respond to a proposal by asking 'what's in it for me?', they are offering the project manager an opportunity to explain why they should support the project.

Alternatively, power can be enhanced through tactics that level the playing field. In health and community services, knowledge and expertise are highly valued, and project leaders who hold or develop a superior knowledge base, and use it to add value for the stakeholders, can enhance their power or influence and thus be more effective in negotiations (Pinto 2000).

In real life, the champions of change juggle opportunities, problems, the shadow side of the organisation and their upward management issues— and a combination of good luck, good ideas and good management gets them through. Whatever model or strategy for change management is used, the 'pointy end' of change management in projects is dealing with the response typically labelled 'resistance'. We use this label in the following sections, but it's important to note that some of what is called resistance to change is motivated by concern about technical errors or wrong-headed policies. A lot of this concern can be met with a listening

Case 8.1 Understanding resistance to change

The consulting doctors whose lives are organised within a complex web of sessional arrangements and a daily round of attendances at private rooms and several hospitals have good practical reasons to resist a proposal for daily morning ward rounds in one of the hospitals in which they work. And the reasons persist even if payment for their time is adequate, and regardless of how much more efficient it might make the care of their patients. They also have the power of their independence, and often that of the market (in other words, they will be hard to replace). Gnashing of managerial teeth, and exhortations to 'think of the greater good', are unlikely to be very persuasive. For change to happen, the consultants' real difficulties and best interests are going to have to be understood and responded to, as the power of the manager to force change is probably limited.

ear, and improvements to project design can result. Not all resistance is motivated by self-interest, nor is it necessarily a threat to the project.

The rationale of resistance

When changes are proposed, the people who will be affected begin calculating gains and losses in relation to two basic questions: 'What's in it for me?' and 'Will it really happen?' There are some good reasons for the tendency to resist change. Those who are comfortable with the way things are will often see, perhaps correctly, that they have something to lose, including some of the power or influence they currently hold. And they will often have some power that they can use in order to resist, as Case 8.1 illustrates.

On the other hand, those who stand to gain from a proposed change, either personally or because they agree with the goals of the change, are in a position of uncertainty. Their active support generally depends not only on whether they can see that there is something in it for them, but also on whether they believe it will really happen.

Resistance can occur anywhere. Individuals and groups without strong power find ways to resist change, and senior managers whose areas are affected by the project might also use tactics of resistance. Some of the direct and indirect approaches to the art of resistance are summarised below (with apologies to the animal world).

The White Ant: Sneaks around pointing out all the possible downsides, no matter how far-fetched or unlikely. Undermines and actively works against change. 'If you go to daylight saving, the cream will curdle, the scones won't rise and the curtains will fade.'

The Beaver: Mobilises resentment about every problem, and every change in living memory, to build a dam of resistance. 'You could let them know how angry you are about the new intake process by helping me to stop them from changing the team structure, and anyway we haven't recovered from the rostering system they put in three years ago.'

The Tortoise: Never comes to meetings about proposals s/he doesn't like the sound of, and doesn't read emails advising how to contribute; moves slowly on everything related to the proposal, and grumbles quietly in the tearoom about not being consulted. 'Don't talk to me, don't change anything without talking to me, and don't move so fast.'

The Kangaroo: Usually a senior manager, hops from one idea to the next, and appears just before sunset wanting to change the project scope. 'You've built a great battleship, now let's make it fly.'

The Red Herring: Finds a very interesting distraction to complicate and bedevil the path of the project. 'The new system will be great, but only if we can reorganise the Christmas holiday roster by Friday.'

Changing resistance

Perhaps one of the most famous models of change is Lewin's force field analysis. Lewin (1958) sees the change process as a struggle between the driving forces for change and the restraining forces for maintaining the status quo.

According to Lewin's model, the change agent should first of all identify through qualitative research the forces for and the forces against the change. An assessment can then be made as to which of the forces is strongest and weakest, and what strategies are needed to support the positives and weaken the negatives. In Figure 8.2, the project is championed by a senior manager, and supported by an effective, confident team (which needs to be sustained through the change process) and a budget imperative. The change could affect staffing numbers, so fear of redundancies is a source of resistance. The senior manager also knows that although the CEO professes support, she will be watching to ensure that the senior manager is kept in line. The senior manager believes this problem can be headed off, so the CEO is therefore listed as a weak force of resistance.

Figure 8.2 Force field analysis

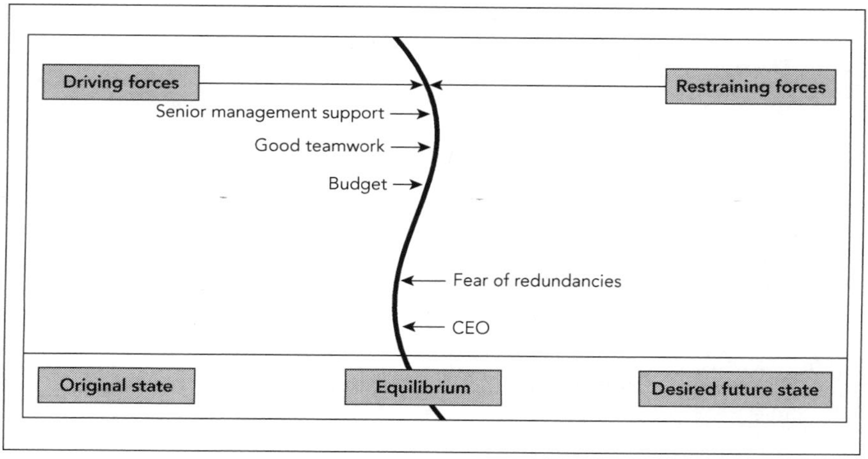

Source: Adapted from Martin & Henderson 2001

Martin and Henderson (2001) point out that 'pull' tactics as well as 'push' can be used to move the line of resistance: sometimes it is more effective to focus on weakening resistance rather than on strengthening the forces for change. For example, the fear of redundancies will not go away because positive forces are strengthened. It is more effectively dealt with directly, by providing cast-iron assurances (if there really will be no redundancies) or by negotiating principles to protect the interests of staff (if redundancies are on the cards). On the other hand, the weak potential for problems with the CEO is best dealt with indirectly through strengthening the positives of trust and accountability in the manager's relationship with the CEO.

The next stage is to 'unfreeze' patterns of behaviour on several levels: the individual, the structures and systems, and the organisational climate/relationships—that is, to make the behaviour patterns less stable, more questionable and more open to change. This is followed by the stage of movement or transition, followed by the 'refreezing' of the new patterns of behaviour and the institutionalisation of change. Lewin recognised that the intervening transition requires careful management and thoughtful implementation tactics.

The value of Lewin's model is that it can be applied to almost any change situation. It provides a way of mapping the hidden forces that can derail the change process and the analytical basis for a strategy for dealing with them. Like the stakeholder analysis map in Chapter 5 (Figure 5.1), it can help the project manager to identify the important resisters who need to be moved, and the important supporters who need to be nurtured and mobilised.

Listening to resistance

There is temptation for the project manager and team to label resistance as a bad thing and to reject it. However, it is likely that at least some of the resistance will be well informed and well intentioned, and potentially valuable for the project—for example, staff members' concern about the costs of change may be based on a more detailed understanding of current reality than the project manager enjoys. Understanding and analysing the sources of resistance, plus the needs and interests of the groups involved, will often lead to change in the project. Each issue must be judged objectively on its merits, and sometimes, project managers need to challenge their own assumptions.

For project managers who lack coercive power, there are two basic ways to shift resisters: buy them off or change their hearts and minds, or both. It may be possible, for example, to convince them that change is needed through well-presented data and analysis. For some people, being brought into the tent (that is, included on committees or in formal and informal meetings) will be enough to move them from mild resistance to open-minded monitoring or even a position of support.

There is usually great value in meeting with stakeholders who are resisting change or opposed to the project. It is much easier in face to face meetings to understand the stakeholder perspective (and assumptions) and genuinely work towards resolving identified issues, as illustrated by Case 8.2.

When project changes are made in response to feedback from stakeholders, the situation should be presented openly and with appreciation. It is the project manager's responsibility to follow through with any needed adjustments to the project plan, including its timetable or strategies.

Case 8.2 illustrates the critical role of communication in both preventing and managing resistance. This is confirmed by recent studies that found 'rich project communications' are a strong factor in project success (Andersen et al. 2006; Chen 2011).

Project bureaucracy and organisational change: a paradox

We have argued throughout this book that project management is all about change. But there are two paradoxes that should be noted. The first is that an overly bureaucratic model of project management might actually impede organisational change (Hodgson 2004, Partington 1996). Emphasis on rigid control through adherence to detailed plans and budgets and tight timelines can work against the emerging iterative nature of many change projects in health and community services. The real solutions to problems in models of care or support systems are often not known at the beginning of a project, which may be why a project approach to the problem has been chosen. In this case, the project team and the stakeholders need to be flexible in their expectations of exactly what will emerge at the other end, how and when. The project plan is still a vital component, but the need to plan for variation is also strong. Project managers must avoid falling in love with their plans and tools.

Case 8.2 'I'm not using that system'

The project was midway through implementing a clinical information system that included electronic prescribing of outpatient medications. Dr Smith, the head of the infectious diseases unit, had so far not accepted any invitations to join the project clinical advisory group, attend system demonstrations or provide any direct feedback to the project team. Word on the grapevine was that Dr Smith had announced her intentions at the hospital's grand round to boycott the new system on the basis that it was a 'bad system' that had failed when implemented at other hospitals.

The project manager initiated a meeting with Dr Smith to understand the issues and perceptions about the system, but also to invite her to participate more actively in the project.

The project manager soon found that both his team and Dr Smith had made some incorrect assumptions. Firstly, Dr Smith had not received the invitations to participate in the project as they had been sent to an old email address. Secondly, Dr Smith clarified that while she had had numerous conversations with colleagues about her concerns about the system, she had not announced her intention to boycott it.

Dr Smith's concerns were about the usability of the system (she had heard reports from another hospital that the system had caused complete chaos in Outpatients) and that using the system to prescribe would take too long, causing increased patient waiting times. She had also been wrongly advised that the prescribing system would not cater for the antibiotic authorisation process.

The project manager then welcomed Dr Smith's input to the project and reiterated the invitation to become involved. The project manager clarified that the team had contacted the other hospital using the system, and that the major issues causing the delay had been related to the location of the prescription printers and the old PCs that they had been using.

The project manager suggested that his team work with Dr Smith and her junior doctors to ensure that the system performs well for infectious diseases prescribing and that the new workflow was optimised. Dr Smith went on to be one of the system's most outspoken advocates.

The second paradox is the fact that senior managers may, in effect, be asked to disempower themselves and at the same time impose more discipline on themselves (Partington 1996). While the organisational change literature argues that support of top management is essential if change is to be realised, in practice there is tension between project-based authority (held by the project sponsor and manager) and the functional authority of line managers. As Partington notes, 'it is natural for managers at every level to struggle against the abandonment of hierarchies' (1996, p. 18).

Projects may also effectively ask managers to exercise their authority differently, and with more discipline. By locking managers as well as staff into specified goals, strategies, deliverables and budgets, projects can be seen as a temporary and partial stay on the ability of senior managers to change their minds and to manage discrete parts of their operations separately and incrementally. In some cases, the leadership level may not have project expertise, and may lack the skills to operate competently in a project environment—for example, not knowing how to respond to the challenges of managing a matrix or juggling both projects and line operations (Partington 1996).

The solution to this second problem is a long-term one that must be tackled by the organisation as a whole. However, the project manager who is aware of these issues can at least understand some of the sources of resistance from above, and at best can design ways of working around them.

Summary

- The implementation phase is where the planned project actions are taken and strategies implemented.
- Project management is a set of methods, but it is also an art that requires flexibility and persistence. Generic project management skills are important to the success of a project, but familiarity with the content of the project and the culture of the organisation is an advantage.
- Both technical project management skills and people skills are required by a good project manager.
- Leadership, motivation and teamwork are essential in creating successful project outcomes, and project managers need team-building skills and the ability to run effective meetings, as well as problem-solving skills.

- Projects are powerful enablers of change, and organisational change theorists suggest that participative approaches to change are likely to be more effective and sustainable than top-down approaches. Senior management needs to set the parameters and explain the 'givens'.
- Managing change is a political process. While some elements of the power structure are overt, many are embedded in the shadow side of the organisation and outside ordinary managerial intervention. Projects can provide an opportunity to bring important issues into the open and deal constructively with the shadow side.
- Change management strategies identified in the project plan are enacted in the implementation phase and require monitoring to assess their effectiveness, and to identify resistance or signs of change fatigue.
- Project managers must listen to and understand the dynamics of resistance to change, paying particular heed to the forces for and against change, and stakeholder groups.

Readings and resources

On implementation:

Agile project management: Project Management Institute, 2017, *A Guide to the Project Management Body of Knowledge* (PMBOK® Guide), 6th edn, Newtown Square, PA: PMI Inc

Change management resources: www.prosci.com/change-management

GRPI model source: Beckhard, R., 1972, www.accipio.com/eleadership/mod/wiki/prettyview.php?pageid=175

Problem solving: www.mediate.com/articles/thicks.cfm

Project implementation: www.mastering-project-management.com/project-plan-execution.html

Turner, J.R., 2007, *Gower Handbook of Project Management*, 4th edn, Burlington, VT: Gower Publishing Limited

On change:

Agile as a change management approach: https://research.hanze.nl/en/publications/agile-development-as-a-change-management-approach-in-healthcare-i

Johnstone, L.P., Dwyer, J. & Lloyd, P.J., 2006, 'Leading and managing change', in M.G. Harris, (ed), *Managing Health Services: Concepts and practice*, 2nd edn, Sydney: Elsevier, pp. 159–80

Participation resource: http://kids.nsw.gov.au/uploads/documents/tps_resources.pdf

9

The implementation phase 2: controlling, completing, closing

> When projects fail or need to be terminated
> Final evaluation
> Learning from the project experience
> The final report
> Sustaining project outcomes
> Conclusion
> Summary
> Readings and resources

This chapter addresses tasks, tools and techniques for controlling and measuring the project's progress to successful completion, and closing and reporting on the project. The separation between the execution tasks (see Chapter 8) and the tasks of maintaining control and monitoring the progress of a project is a little artificial: control and monitoring play a key role in making the project happen, and the twists and turns of implementation can either support or challenge effective control and monitoring.

Control and monitoring during implementation

Controlling a project is about ensuring that its objectives are met by monitoring and measuring progress regularly to identify variances from the plan—and taking corrective action when it is needed (PMI 2017, pp. 105–7). Methods and tools are important for control and monitoring, and decisions should be made as early as possible about which ones will be used. Some organisations have mandated methods that they use for this purpose, and in others there is flexibility about mixing and matching tools according to the needs of the project. Project managers may need to import or develop their own templates, forms and data collection and reporting processes. Some are provided in the project templates section at the end of this book.

The information for a good control system should be visible, accurate, reliable, valid, timely and both diagnostic (what is happening?) and prognostic (what impact will it have?). And it should be tailored to the needs of the project on the basis of the project plan. The plan will normally cover all the project parameters that require monitoring, and hence enable the design of a reporting and monitoring system. The evaluation plan will also highlight the required areas of focus for data collection and analysis. Although exactly what needs to be monitored relies heavily on the nature of the project, it is likely that data on expenditure (compared to budget), task/activity completion (compared to the schedule) and performance (compared to the specifications) will be monitored. Meredith and Mantel (2012) suggest that while it is easy to focus on monitoring data that are easily gathered, monitoring should concentrate primarily on measuring important indicators of output (for example, the extent to which system design has been completed), rather than on intensity of activity (for example, the number of meetings that have been held).

There are several aspects of any project that will be challenging to monitor and control. We briefly address controlling the scope and schedule, the budget and resources, project quality, risk and contingencies, before turning to the challenge of managing projects when they get into trouble.

Keeping to the plan

Having seen that the project is well planned and scoped, the project manager must then ensure that the project progresses as smoothly as possible according to the project plan (unless variations are agreed). The amount and quality of project planning will quickly become evident in the implementation phase. Any deficiency in planning may not be the project manager's doing, as not all project managers have the benefit of being involved in the project from the beginning—but the project manager is the one who will deal with the consequences.

The tasks of planning, monitoring and controlling are cyclical. That is, the cycle of planning, checking on progress, comparing progress to the plan and taking corrective action if progress does not match the plan is followed by another round of planning to incorporate any necessary changes (Meredith & Mantel 2012).

The general methods for monitoring adherence to plans are status collection and assessment against the baseline provided by the plan. The defined information to measure the progress of both the entire project and the activities within it can be collected in many ways. Data and information on what is actually happening in the project range from financial reports showing actual costs versus budget, to timeliness of care data generated in the Emergency Department's routine systems, to 'corridor chat' about emerging issues. When the data generated are meaningful and reasonably accurate, the information can be a powerful impetus towards goal attainment—achieving milestones and outcomes—for teams and stakeholders.

Controlling project scope—change control

During the implementation phase in any project, changes to the plan ('variances' or 'variations') are normal and to be expected. If there are significant variances (and they jeopardise the project objectives), the plan can be adjusted by repeating the relevant planning process—for example, re-estimating the staffing levels. It is almost inevitable that as soon as the project plan and scope have been written and signed off, changes will occur. The important issue for control is to ensure that variances are documented, the plan is adjusted accordingly, and the variance is formally accepted by the authorised group or individual.

The scope that was agreed, planned for and documented in the planning phase may be challenged or require modification for legitimate reasons. There could be a change to the contract, the deliverables, the target implementation group, the budget and the schedule, to name a few. For example, during an information system implementation, there may be a need to include further functionality in order for the system to work; or the timing for a go-live might need to be extended to ensure that all the defects and issues are fixed. However, 'scope creep' (unmanaged expansion of the project's scope) is a common and serious threat, leading to cost blowouts, missed deadlines and unmet expectations.

The tools to manage and control project scope include:
- a change request process, most commonly using a change request form (see Template 9.1)
- a process for assessing the project impact of the change request, such as impact on the budget or schedule
- formal review and approval of change requests by the steering committee, which then gives authority to the project manager to revise the project accordingly, or decline to do so.

When the project is being conducted by external consultants, the contract will usually include a provision for variations. This protects the consultant from escalating costs due either to fickle decision-making by the client or to genuine contingencies arising in the project, things not reasonably foreseen. The contract will also usually contain clauses that enable the client to extract additional work if the variation is of the consultant's making (for example, poor modelling) or to reduce or withhold payments if the quality standards are not met.

Controlling the project schedule

A chart or graphical display is the most common and simplest way to represent data in order to monitor and control a project. A bar or line graph can easily show progress in each aspect of a project compared with the project plan. Virtually any aspect of a project can be measured, and the priority is to chart the critical factors for project success. Items that are often charted in this way include:

- project task progress (percentage completion of project tasks as a whole by week)
- staff utilisation (for example, percentage usage by week)
- performance (for example, number and magnitude of variations)
- task hours and percentage complete
- customer satisfaction measures or milestones.

For projects that are structured in stages, the finishing of one stage, sign-off and commencement of the next is another opportunity for controlling the scope and schedule. At the commencement of the new stage, progress and the potential for variations can be reviewed, as demonstrated in Figure 9.1.

Controlling the budget and resources

The estimation and budgeting of project costs (see Chapter 7) is difficult and often poorly done, which can mean in turn that it is difficult to control the costs of a project against the plan. Also, if the budget is not altered when the scope of a project changes, there is little chance that the costs will match it.

Monitoring of actual and forecast expenditure against budget is probably one of the most familiar control tools in the management toolkit. Good information is an important aid to the control of costs, but in the end hard decisions may be required. There are several kinds of contingency response that might be called on—finding other sources of funding, reducing the scope, taking up the slack in one part of the project to support another part's shortfall, or moving team members around to meet priority needs.

Figure 9.1 Schedule for developing online learning modules

% Work Complete	Task Name	Duration	Start	Finish
100%	Concept Phase	17 days	Mon 4/06	Tue 26/06
100%	Planning Phase	21 days	Tue 26/06	Tue 24/07
0%	Implementation Phase	36 days	Wed 25/07	Wed 12/09
0%	**Stage 1 eLearning Modules**	19 days	Wed 25/07	Mon 20/08
100%	Drafting of eLearning modules 1–3	5 days	Wed 25/07	Tue 31/07
100%	Development of eLearning modules 1–3	5 days	Wed 1/08	Tue 7/08
0%	Testing of Stage 1 modules	3 days	Wed 8/08	Fri 10/08
0%	Communication to students	1 day	Mon 13/08	Mon 13/08
0%	Stage 1 modules go-live	1 day	Mon 13/08	Mon 13/08
0%	Evaluation of modules by user survey	5 days	Tue 14/08	Mon 20/08
0%	*Sign off Stage 1 modules*	0 days	Mon 20/08	Mon 20/08
0%	**Stage 2 eLearning Modules**	17 days	Fri 17/08	Wed 12/09
0%	Drafting of eLearning modules 4–8	4 days	Tue 21/08	Fri 24/08
0%	Development of modules 4–8	4 days	Mon 27/08	Thu 30/08
0%	Testing of Stage 2 modules	2 days	Fri 31/08	Mon 3/09
0%	Communication to students	1 day	Tue 4/09	Tue 4/09
0%	Stage 2 modules go-live	1 day	Wed 5/09	eLearning Wed 5/09
0%	Evaluation of modules by user survey	5 days	Thu 6/09	Wed 12/09
0%	*Sign off Stage 2 modules*	0 days	Wed 12/09	Wed 12/09
0%	**Project Close**	2 days	Thu 13/09	Fri 14/09

Managing quality

When projects are in the implementation phase, the pressure to cut corners in order to maintain progress may be significant. If performance criteria have been defined in the planning phase (see Chapter 5), the focus during implementation is firstly to ensure that they are made explicit and understood by all stakeholders. This is one of the reasons why it is a good idea to set up quality assurance mechanisms that are transparent and require reporting to the sponsor or project steering committee on a regular basis.

The second focus of quality monitoring is to ensure that any variation from the quality plan is logged, documented and resolved at a high level. A procedure for acceptance of variations to the quality plan (change requests) should be formalised (usually through the project steering committee, or the sponsor).

Some project teams appoint a 'quality partner': a friendly expert adviser/auditor who takes a watching brief, not waiting for the documentation of problems, but working confidentially with the team to prevent them. An experienced project manager or a person with expertise in quality in the relevant area could play this role.

Managing risk and contingency

During the implementation phase, the risk plan and the risk register (a log of project risk events) should be regularly reviewed and updated, with existing risks reviewed and reassessed, and newly identified risks added. High and major risks should be reported to the sponsor or project steering committee via the agreed reporting processes (see Template 5.1, the project status report, at the end of the book); if risk events occur, they should be reported immediately and the planned response initiated. For major risks, this will almost certainly require 'escalating' the problem to the required level of organisational authority.

Managing evaluation

The project plan should include an evaluation plan, outlining how the project will be evaluated: what are the criteria for judging success, on what data or evidence will that assessment be made, and how will it be collected and analysed? (See Chapter 6.)

The evaluation plan may include process evaluation—periodic assessment of the effectiveness of the processes the project uses—for example, the extent to which stakeholders are engaged in and supportive of the project. Progressive evaluation and reporting of evaluation findings according to project stages or milestones may be needed, as not all deliverables require that you wait to the end of the project to evaluate them. Reporting periodically on interim project successes may also assist with maintaining momentum for the project, informing later project stages and strengthening stakeholder support.

The collection of process evaluation data need not be intrusive (or worse, destabilising). Minutes of meetings, as well as qualitative assessment by the team, sponsor and perhaps quality partner, can be used to garner information—as can indicators such as levels of attendance at meetings and capacity of the committee to make decisions in a timely way.

The work of implementing the evaluation plan should be built in as much as possible to the project's routine record-keeping and processes, so that the needed information and evidence on which a summative assessment can be made is available when the project is at completion.

Status reporting

The purpose of a status report is to advise the steering committee, project sponsor and other stakeholders whether the project is on track to deliver the planned outcomes, and to highlight where their decision-making or direct help is needed. Regular status reporting helps to ensure that the team has a clear view of the true state of the project, and that management stays properly informed about project progress, difficulties and issues by periodically getting the right kinds of information from the project manager. Frequent communication of project status and issues is a vital part of effective project risk management. A status report can be a formal document that is presented at meetings, or it can be a regular email or verbal update to key stakeholders.

Status reporting can commence as early in the project as required—for example, in the concept or planning phase—and early reporting can assist in both managing risk and keeping the project on the radar of important stakeholders, including senior management. The frequency of status reporting will vary depending on the size of the project and the requirements of the steering committee or project sponsor. It is possible to provide too much detail in status reports, which can overwhelm busy project stakeholders—the net effect being that they do not read the report or know what to action. It is important to identify and define the indicators that the project is using (for example, red, amber or green 'traffic lights', also known as **RAG reporting**) to enable stakeholders to quickly understand the status of the project.

There are many status-report templates available on the internet (for example, at www.projectconnections.com), and your organisation may already have a template in use. It is also a good idea to check with the project sponsor and the steering committee on their requirements for status reporting, as they may prefer the information presented in a particular way. Template 5.1 at the end of the book outlines the information that is commonly documented in a project status report.

Some projects also require the development of a benefits realisation plan (see Chapter 6 and NSW Government [2018]), that will need to be updated and finalised during the implementation phase.

When things go wrong: getting back in control

If there is going to be trouble in a project, it tends to rise to the surface during the implementation phase. Sometimes the problems relate directly back to the project design and plan. Perhaps the stakeholder issues are not resolvable, or the decision to proceed in the first place was not a wise one, or the political environment in the organisation is not supportive. Often, the ability of the project manager to handle unexpected crises and deviations from the plan is the determining factor in whether a project is successful or succumbs to the problems that arise during its life.

So, when is a project in trouble? The project's monitoring and control activities should provide the project manager with the information required to know its status and its progress towards objectives at regular intervals. The earlier that signs of trouble are detected, the more effectively they can be dealt with. As noted above, one effective way of avoiding nasty surprises is to have regular status reporting both from and to the project team, the steering committee or other stakeholder groups, and the customer or sponsor.

The concrete nature of the project plan (or contract) is intended as a discipline for the sponsor or the client as well as for the team. For internal projects, the project plan or the charter can act like a contract, and assist the team to resist unnecessary or harmful 'good ideas' from above.

If problems are emerging, interactions with the project team, the sponsor and stakeholders will contain warning signs that the project manager needs to assess and respond to. Examples of warning signs that may jeopardise a project include:

- essential support systems are not working or are significantly behind schedule
- senior management is not delivering on promised interventions (such as mandating requirements for staff to participate in training in new systems or procedures)
- the project itself is falling behind schedule to a point where agreed project deliverables will not be met
- essential resources (such as provision of IT services) are not forthcoming
- stakeholders fail to turn up to important meetings, or the sponsor or steering committee members are habitually unavailable
- a key quality indicator is not met (for example, a failed software test)
- the need for the project outcome is fading because of external changes, or it is losing internal priority

- the project team is dysfunctional
- a key person is lost to the project
- the project objectives are looking unachievable—the outcome will not be sustainable (or profitable), or the service or product will not work well enough.

If signs like these are emerging, decisive action is probably required. Escalating the issue—taking it higher in the organisation—should not be seen by the project manager as a failure, given that many issues arising during the life of the project will be beyond their control. An escalation process and criteria may be defined in the project plan, and can be as informal as calling the project sponsor to brief them and request advice, or be dealt with more formally at a steering committee meeting. In some cases, there will be a need to rethink and either change the project or close it down. In other cases, the project manager will need to pull out all stops and 'press on' through a tight spot.

The best outcome for a troubled project may, in fact, be to terminate it before further investments are made or additional costs are incurred (for example, through industrial action, which damages good relations between management and staff).

Most successful project managers have war stories about projects that succeeded only after great adversity. Sometimes adversity is a necessary struggle to resolve an unknown factor or an error in the project design, and in the end it improves the project—though it may also add to the project manager's grey hair.

Project completion

Sooner or later, all projects come to an end. For some, closure comes with a sense of celebration and achievement. For others, closure takes place prematurely in an atmosphere of high drama, anger and blame. Projects can also drift along aimlessly until they are quietly killed off when no-one is looking. Sometimes projects that have been applauded on completion are found to be wanting when their outcomes are evaluated. Conversely, projects that appear to have failed can prove their worth at a much later stage. And for projects that set up and trial a new service or process, there is always the question of sustainability: will it continue when the project is finally over and there is no project manager in the driving seat?

This is the final phase of the project life cycle. First, we focus on the practical tasks of project completion, followed by a discussion of the dilemmas involved in the premature closure of projects. We then turn to finalising the evaluation, and ensuring important information about the processes, outputs and outcomes of the project is documented.

When is a project finished?

The operational definition of project success, like the project itself, is unique. While the generic 'iron triangle' of cost, time and specifications is a useful reference point, real projects have more flavour and texture, as well as outcomes that go beyond the project deliverables. Stakeholders tend to assess success based on their interests and perspectives. For example, there is evidence that 'top management support', usually cited as something you need for success, is often a dominant *measure* of success—that is, the project is a success if the leaders believe it to be so (Shokri-Ghasabeh & Kavousi-Chabok 2009).

When a project has run its course, the process of completing and closing it (sometimes called '**close-out**') is an important final step. The criteria for project completion are defined (explicitly or implicitly) in the project plan, typically as the finishing of all tasks in the plan, and the achievement of planned outcomes and deliverables.

The nature of the completion tasks and their timing will vary, but they fall into three main categories: acceptance and handover (the practical completion), completing the evaluation and the final report. If a project is to be quietly buried, the completion tasks are somewhat different.

Acceptance and handover

Acceptance and handover is the process of presenting deliverables to the project sponsor (and/or the steering committee or the person/team who will take over responsibility for the ongoing operation of the project outcomes) and getting sign-off or formal acceptance. This process also includes completing all necessary documentation and leaving project files in good order (including proper storage of data collected by the project), winding up the project team and the office, and celebrating success.

Acceptance of the project outcomes or deliverables by the authorised person or group is a key milestone, and acceptance certificates (commonly used for ICT system or software acceptance) may be required to document this formally. See Template 9.2 at the back of the book for an example, or go to www.slideshare.net/demand metric/project-acceptance-document. Practical handover of a working or satisfactory outcome should be formalised, even for the smallest and simplest projects. Recognition of the work, and clarity about acceptance (including any residual issues), are important for all who have contributed and for those who will work with the project's outcomes.

A final meeting with the steering committee and/or the project sponsor is a common method for acceptance and handover. Such a meeting can also deal with tying up any loose ends. The project might have brought into focus issues that are outside its scope to resolve and which need to be handed over—for example, participants in community consultations may have identified concerns unrelated to the project that require a response by the agency. There might also be a need to ensure allocation of responsibility for ongoing implementation of the project's outcomes, and for communication about the project while the new process or product is being bedded down.

There may be aspects of the project's deliverables that cannot be wrapped up at the time of completion. A key piece of equipment or software needed for the full operation of a new service might not yet be available, or the industrial implications of a change might have to be sorted out in a different timeframe. These issues need to be clearly identified, a process for resolving them agreed, and interim arrangements to work around the outstanding issues made.

A debriefing process—that is, an opportunity for people to discuss their experiences and impressions of the project—can be rewarding in itself, and can also provide input to the evaluation and the final report. Members of the steering committee and other key stakeholders, as well as the team, might appreciate both formal and informal opportunities to reflect and debrief.

The team also needs to wind up, even if some members will go on together to work on another project or become part of the ongoing operating team. The project office may need to be closed, and its equipment distributed to the appropriate areas (or returned to the Project Management Office). Individuals sometimes need assistance in the transition back to their old jobs, or in moving on to new ones. Recognition of the transition, and practical assistance, can make it easier. Preparations for this process made in the early stages, and good management of team members, will pay off at this point.

Finally, there is a need for celebration. The effort and commitment, as well as the achievements, of those who have contributed to a successful outcome need to be recognised. A special edition of the agency's newsletter, recording and celebrating the project's outcomes, might be released. A formal handover meeting might end with refreshments and thanks to all involved. The 'go-live' point for a new system delivered by the project can also be the occasion for celebration. Celebrations of success can be a good way of building or maintaining a positive climate, and can consolidate the pride and satisfaction people feel in their work and their organisation. Parties can also be important when the news is not good, as Case 9.1 shows.

When projects fail or need to be terminated

In our experience, the survivors of failed projects usually attribute failure to inadequacies in the planning, prioritising and resourcing of projects. Failure to define the goals and scope well enough, with the result that the project goes 'off track' and is then hard to stop, is a typical story.

The reasons for project failure are in many ways the mirror image of the predictors of success. For example, the UK National Audit Office (Parliamentary Office of Science and Technology 2003, p. 8), following a review of IT projects in the public sector, listed these factors:

- lack of a clear link between the project and the organisation's key strategic priorities, including agreed measures of success
- lack of clear ownership and leadership by senior management and/or ministers
- lack of effective engagement with stakeholders
- lack of skills or a proven approach to project management and risk management
- lack of understanding of, and contact with, the supply industry at senior levels in the organisation
- evaluation of proposals driven by initial price rather than long-term value for money (especially securing delivery of business benefits)
- too little attention given to breaking development and implementation into manageable steps
- inadequate resources and skills for delivery of all the required outcomes.

If a project hasn't succeeded, or is limping along without a clear path to completion, the best course of action may be to abandon or discontinue it. Projects can fail in many ways, ranging from escalation

Case 9.1 Recognising handover in an outsourcing project

The hotel services staff (cleaners, caterers, porters and couriers) of a large health agency had struggled against outsourcing, and had put up an in-house bid (a proposal to keep the service in-house on new terms), which had failed. Most of them had been offered jobs by the successful bidder, but there was a lot of sadness and some anger—particularly for the long-serving staff, some of whom had been with the organisation from its beginning, and felt that they had always done a good job.

Care had been taken throughout the project to offer support to the staff, to keep them regularly informed of progress, to facilitate access to independent financial advice, to maximise their opportunities for ongoing employment and to assist those who missed out. The human resources department argued that this approach should be sustained to the end, and that there should be a farewell party for all the staff, whether they were leaving or transferring to the new employer. The general manager agreed, but approached the occasion with dread.

The usual form was to be followed—food and drink, gifts— and a short speech was definitely part of the agenda. With his heart in his mouth, the GM spoke of the good work and loyalty of the staff, as well as acknowledging that the policy requiring competitive tendering of support services was deeply unpopular and that the staff had been through a time of uncertainty and anxiety about their futures. He finished by expressing the good wishes of the hospital community. The applause was muted, and the mood sombre, but it was clear that the staff appreciated this proper farewell with the usual courtesies extended. This formal, respectful recognition of the moment of transition may also have contributed to the good working relationships that were experienced under the new contract.

('just one more extra mile to go') through to seismic shifts in the environment. For example, in a time of national health reform, restructuring of the public health system may mean that many innovation projects are halted or abandoned because of the disruption to teams, plans and decision-making, and/or the departure of project champions. When the barriers are insurmountable, or when rescue efforts have failed, the only alternative may be to terminate the project, discontinue the work and reassign the people who were working on it. Closing a project can also be a planned contingency—for example, when the findings in one stage of a project indicate a fatal flaw in its design or feasibility, and the decision not to proceed with further stages is the only option.

Terminating a project prior to its planned conclusion is difficult, because it usually involves the curtailing of a previously held vision, the breaking up of a 'project family' and perhaps the admission of failure. Termination of a project may simply mean that a project no longer continues in its current form. Meredith and Mantel (2012) examined the varieties of project termination, calling them extinction, addition, integration and starvation. *Extinction* means the project is stopped (whether successful or unsuccessful). *Addition* means that the project is incorporated into ongoing operations as a distinct unit or department in the organisation. *Integration* is where the project disappears but elements of it are distributed within the organisation, and *starvation* is where the project still exists but budget cuts mean that no progress is achieved. An example of a project made extinct is illustrated in Case 9.2.

Case 9.2 Project cancelled

The project manager identified warning signs in the early days of a project that aimed to upgrade an existing intensive care unit (ICU) information system. Though the system was well out of date (about three major versions behind), and the software vendor had advised that they no longer supported the old version, the new ICU management team had shown little interest in an upgrade project. The medical director (the project sponsor) had escalated the risk regarding the critical software being unsupported, and requested that the IT project manager work with the ICU staff to develop the business case for a system upgrade.

In drafting the business case, the project manager discovered that there was little support for the existing ICU system, with ICU management actively investigating systems to replace it. They felt that upgrading the current system was a waste of time, effort and money.

The project manager completed and submitted the business case (with the information that ICU had provided), but also advised that there had been lack of stakeholder buy-in. The project sponsor agreed that a new system was desirable, but believed that there was not enough money, and informed the ICU staff that the upgrade of the current system was going ahead.

The project was therefore put in motion with the business case signed off, software vendor engaged and planning workshops held. It was not until the project team was being established, with the secondment of ICU staff, that ICU management moved from passive to active resistance. One after another, the ICU manager assigned people to the project who were variously not interested, had little knowledge of the current system or were paid significantly more than was estimated in the business case. Then there was the issue of releasing them from the ICU roster, which involved a delay of up to six weeks.

The CEO was concerned about resulting variations to the project plan and timelines, and lobbying by ICU management further destabilised support for the project. The straw that broke the camel's back was a forecast overrun on the budget. The chief finance officer stepped in and announced that the project would be cancelled forthwith. The project manager disbanded the team and thanked them all for their efforts.

Sometimes commitment to a project means that efforts to revive and sustain it continue well beyond reasonable limits. In a major study of escalation (ever-expanding duration and cost) in IT projects, Keil et al. (2000) surveyed 2500 information systems audit and control professionals. The reported rate of escalation in IT projects was 30 to 40 per cent, and once escalation started, ultimate success was much less likely. The best explanation for the tendency to persist with failing projects in this study was the 'completion effect'. That is, projects are more likely to continue when those making decisions believe that they are so close to completion that persistence is justified regardless of additional cost. The implication is that once an IT project begins seriously to fail, it is probably best to let it go.

Termination is not necessarily the same thing as failure, but poor management of the process can make things worse. While it is never easy, once the decision is made it should be done quickly to minimise further waste of resources and disruption to the organisation. It is almost always a good idea to develop and articulate a clear statement of reasons for termination, and proactively communicate this message to all concerned, without delay and as consistently as possible. This tactic will not stop rumours, but it will at least ensure that they are not circulated in a vacuum. The rights and interests of the staff involved need to be protected with clear and prompt action.

One exit method for a project that is limping to a dead end is simply to declare it finished: adopt a modified goal that has been achieved and cut the losses, with as much dignity as possible. Recommendations for follow-up activity might be made, and evaluation might enable the team and organisation to learn from the experience. The team should be thanked for their efforts and then resettled, with perhaps an opportunity for the drowning of sorrows.

Final evaluation

Preparation for evaluation (see Chapter 6) pays off as the project draws to a close, and the needed analysis of results can be more easily completed. Increasingly, tailored methods of evaluation are being mandated, particularly for larger projects—**Post-Implementation Review (PIR)** and benefits realisation studies being among the best known. Even if planning for evaluation was not done, the project plan provides an implicit basis for evaluation, and can be used for this purpose when necessary. In essence, this means that the project manager writes a simple evaluation plan based on the project's goals and objectives, and uses available data as well as reflection and review activities.

Learning from the project experience

Reflection and learning are always happening during projects. Project managers, team members and stakeholders are engaged in figuring out how to do something new, or how to do something in a new way—so, usually, their minds are engaged at least some of the time in problem-solving and assessment of options. In the closing stages, many project participants will welcome an opportunity to engage in reflection and discussion, and are likely to be doing it in staffrooms, (or bars) anyway.

Some process questions can be answered with information that the project itself supplies:

- Did that approval happen on time?
- Was the report well received by the executive, sponsor and partners?
- Was the project plan modified during the course of the project?
- Did the vendor respond readily to our variance requests?
- Did the steering committee meet regularly with enough people?

For information about why things happened the way they did, other sources are usually needed, and the data or information is usually qualitative in nature:

- Were the stakeholders satisfied that their views were considered and given weight?
- Were our team meetings successful in coordinating the work of the team members, and why?
- Was the communication strategy successful, and why?
- Did any changes to the plan contribute to the project's successful completion?
- Were there any difficulties that the project team encountered, and how were they overcome?

The methods of collecting the qualitative data and information generally rely on asking people the right questions in ways that enable them to be as honest and constructive as possible with the minimum possible time and effort. Face-to-face communication generally (but not always, and not for everyone) yields richer results. People think as they speak, or as they listen to others' views, and the struggle to articulate their experience helps them to understand it better and inform the evaluator more reliably. Anonymous but methodical collection of responses to questions by means of surveys can generate information that might be hard to obtain in person.

Recommendations and learnings gathered from the project manager, team and stakeholders can be captured in a **lessons learned log** throughout and after a project. Lessons learned logs capture both the positive and negative experiences of a project, and give project managers the opportunity to learn from the actual experiences of others, while also demonstrating the organisation's commitment to project management excellence (Rowe & Sikes 2006). An example of a lessons learned log can be found at www.projectmanagementdocs.com/project-closing-templates/lessons-learned.html#axzz5PzJqdhif.

As the project draws to a close, project sponsors and managers often need to look beyond the immediate concrete project goal (essentially, did we make it happen?), and consider the larger benefits realisation question of whether the project's results will deliver the results in practice that inspired the creation of the project.

This question varies greatly according to the type of project. Many projects in health and community services are merely the first step, the initiation and testing of an innovation in ongoing operations or program delivery. So if the project did achieve its immediate goals—the concept was proven, the trial was successful; or the information system is in and working—the more significant question becomes 'will it deliver the benefits we seek?'. Sometimes, this question can be answered at least provisionally in the project's final report, but even so the real test comes in routine operations.

These long-term questions will have been included in a good evaluation plan, perhaps using PIR, but can't be answered in the closing phase of the project due to timing. Making sure that the business of answering them is identified as a future activity, and that responsibility is allocated, is one of the tasks at completion and handover.

If the benefits realisation or PIR methods are being used for the project, an updated plan may need to be prepared by the project manager, perhaps with assistance from finance and information staff. It will update the original benefits realisation/PIR plan with information about progress towards achieving the intended benefits at the time of project closure; factors likely to affect success over the coming review period; and any needed changes to the method or targets (for example, ways of measuring productivity gains, or the period over which they will be realised). This updated plan should also include details as to how—and by whom—monitoring will be undertaken and final assessment made. The updated plan is then part of the formal handover of the project. A process for the approval and implementation of any recommendations for change in the benefits realisation/PIR assessment will be needed.

The final report

The final report is an important element in closing a project and summing it up, either as part of acceptance and handover, or as part of the PIR. Usually written by the project manager, the final report details the overall project at the point of completion and is useful as:

- a historical record of the project and what it achieved
- an opportunity for reflection on the project as a whole
- a comparison of the project at completion with the plan
- a way of informing stakeholders of the status of any outstanding issues
- a record of recommendations for future projects and strategies for sustaining the outcomes of this project
- a summary of the project evaluation, and the learning from it, with the aim of promoting enhanced capability for subsequent projects.

A good final report is structured so that the reader can quickly get a clear overview, can easily find particular information of interest, and doesn't get lost in the detail. While the size and structure of the report will depend on the nature of the project, the sections or headings shown in the Final Report Template 9.3 at the back of this book provide a useful starting point.

The project report should not be structured as a chronological record of the project process (the 'what I did on my holidays' approach). Rather, it should be logically structured in a way that best meets the knowledge and decision-making needs of the readers, avoids repetition, enables the reader to assess the quality and import of the information and data, and hopefully persuades readers to agree with the team's conclusions and recommendations.

If the report needs to help those responsible for implementing or sustaining the project's outcomes, it should focus on the practical and operational aspects of effective implementation. This would usually include the conditions under which the outcomes work well, and the minimum requirements for effective ongoing operations.

If the report needs to convince decision-makers to adopt a proposed change or sustain a project outcome, the logic of its structure should be designed to lead the reader to agree with its proposals and conclusions. If the report is needed to meet the accountability requirements of a funding body (including corporate head office), the author needs to be aware of what their expectations are, and strive to meet them.

A well-written report is a lot more convincing than one that leaves the reader to disentangle spelling errors, poor grammar and unclear meaning. Writing the contents page first is one way to focus on clear, logical structuring (Template 9.3 provides a starting list that can then be varied to fit the project). Some writers find it useful to outline the report first, using dot points, while others prefer to draft whole sections or paragraphs and move them around later if necessary. For most people, there is no real substitute for drafting, reading (and preferably getting others to read) and redrafting.

The project report may need to conform to a house style for documents. The sources of ideas and assertions in the report should be acknowledged, something that is becoming more important as agencies pursue the goals of evidence-based practice and evidence-informed decision-making. There are many acceptable referencing styles, and the agency may have a preferred style. The most important thing is to use it consistently, including for information and documents found on the internet.

If there is a wealth of important detail, it should be organised into attachments so that the data are available for those who need it (perhaps in the form of a separate volume with limited circulation). If the report has a practical use after the life of the project, it may be worthwhile to budget for a professional editor—readability can be significantly improved at a fairly modest cost.

For some projects, or some organisations, simpler documentation may be required, perhaps little more than a set of presentation slides. In any organisation, a clear, concise presentation is an effective way of communicating the project's outcomes and implications, and is a valuable adjunct to the written report. It can be worthwhile doing this well, as a good presentation can be used repeatedly to ensure that a clear, consistent message about the project is communicated to all those affected or interested in its outcomes.

Sustaining project outcomes

Sustaining the project outcomes can be difficult when the project team disperses and funding is exhausted. One of the reasons for this lies in the way funding is secured and dreams are pursued. When resources are scarce, organisations sometimes enact their pursuit of better or bigger services using small dollops of project funding in order to make a start. Then they are likely to face the problem of a long journey, requiring ongoing support and resources they don't have.

The question of sustainability should be addressed at the concept stage, and dispassionate decisions are needed at that point. While there are good reasons for taking big risks very occasionally, to do so routinely is to dissipate energy, reputation, capacity and support. There are many aspects of sustainability that the project itself cannot influence— emerging budget problems, for example. But the project method can make a difference in at least one way: by maximising the engagement of those who will be responsible for ongoing operations. If members of the future operational team are involved in the project concept, design, planning and implementation, they are more likely to be enthusiastic implementers of the outcomes.

Where the project is someone else's good idea, or is operated in a way that excludes or frustrates the receiving team, sustainability is more likely to be a rocky road. This has implications for the way in which PMOs or other central project units conduct their work, and empha-sises again the importance of skilled engagement with stakeholders and recognition of their legitimate interests in the detailed working arrange-ments that the project will later seek to hand over to them.

We have also discussed the use of projects as seduction: persuading others to act by showing how a good idea can work in practice. If such a project succeeds, its existence changes the balance of probabilities (by increasing the intangible costs of denying needed funds) when ongoing resources are being divided up. Case 9.3 illustrates the point.

A successful project can also work to improve the chances of a supportive policy decision being made. It is easier for governments or health authorities to make policy supporting innovative services, or interventions in social problems, if they can point to the results of a successful trial. The success of needle exchange programs in reducing the rate of HIV infection among intravenous drug users is an example of this—the idea of handing out equipment for use in an illegal activity is otherwise hard to justify.

While there are many excellent examples of this strategy—'show it can work and then get the money (or the policy change)'—embarking on this course is a significant risk. It should be done knowingly, for very good reasons, and as an exception not the rule.

Case 9.3 Sustaining the unsustainable

An emergency response service was established with project funding in a teaching hospital. It was based in the emergency department, and mobilised resources to support emergency patients who didn't need an acute admission but couldn't go home without immediate support. It was funded as a project on the attractive theory that if it worked, it would save the hospital costs (by preventing admissions) and would therefore be self-sustaining. The project was evaluated by a major consulting firm, which found that the funding hypothesis was correct in the sense that enough admissions were avoided to cover the direct costs of providing the service. They also found that the money was not, in fact, available for transfer to pay for the service, because the number of admissions to the hospital was not reduced—other patients took the place of those assisted by the service.

However, the service was very popular with patients (who were able to go home with support) and with staff (who were able to move more patients through the emergency department in a timely manner), and it helped the hospital to meet its NEAT (Emergency Admissions) targets. It had also been given positive coverage in the local media and was written up in an academic journal. Some of the patients became aware that the funding base was fragile and lobbied for its continuation, and this happened more than once. The end result was that the service was sustained on repeated rounds of temporary funding for at least five years.

Conclusion

Throughout this book, we have emphasised the need for genuine organisational commitment to the project, for a well-developed and feasible project plan, and for adequate resources and a high-performing project team. We found that, in practice, project management in a complex industry is not just a set of competencies that can be taught from a manual but, rather, requires flexibility, understanding and good judgement.

Good judgement is not something that can be learned from a textbook; good judgement comes from experience and a willingness to reflect and learn from that experience. As Legge, Stanton and Smyth (2006, p. 15) point out, 'Where managers have real choices they cannot *know* the right answer; they have to rely on their judgment (and this means taking risks).'

However, taking risks can be tempered through reflection on practice—on what worked and what did not—and the ability to recognise the patterns or similarities in past experiences that might help to guide the project team in dealing with a current dilemma. The more we reflect and learn from our personal practice, the greater chance we have of making improved decisions when faced with complex situations.

When the first edition of this book was published, we expressed three hopes about the future in project management. The first was greater uptake of project approaches by organisations that face innovation and implementation challenges. As we finish this third edition, it is clear that this hope has been realised, and the sector is now a much more sophisticated, mature and effective user of project management.

The second was that more leaders and managers might accept the discipline of project management in their own approaches to managing change and development. We have seen progress in this area, with greater clarity and openness about goals and methods of change, willingness to support skill development, better understanding that 'the devil is in the detail', and greater respect for the real work of project teams.

The third was that using project management as a way of 'getting good ideas to work' would mean that organisations were better able to achieve their goals and meet the needs of their stakeholders. This remains the major purpose of this book, and its success is in the hands of the reader.

Summary

- Control and monitoring of the progress of project activities (according to the plan) is a key activity in the implementation phase, and there are various methods and tools available to do this. The aspects that are monitored during the implementation phase include project scope, schedule, budgets, resources, quality (or performance), risk and contingency.
- Controlling project scope and managing project variance are key activities.

- Implementation includes enacting the evaluation plan and collecting and analysing the required data. Evaluation may be conducted and reported periodically throughout the project if required.
- During implementation, the project manager will be required to regularly report on the status and progress of the project.
- The project manager might see warning signs of trouble for the project, and may need to escalate or take these issues higher in the organisation in order to resolve them.
- Project closure is an important step in the project life cycle and needs to be actively managed. This phase includes acceptance and handover of the project outcomes and deliverables to the authorised person or group.
- Activities in project closure also include a final meeting and the submission of a final report. Recognising and celebrating the efforts and achievements of those involved in the project, and planning for life after the project, are important.
- Post-Implementation Review, and some of the activities of the benefits realisation plan, may need to be conducted after project closure.
- Projects can fail for a variety of reasons, and may require termination. While closing a failed project can be difficult, once failure is clear, closure should be prompt and decisive.
- Sustaining the outcomes of a project can be difficult, but is more likely where members of the future operational team are involved in the project concept, design, planning and implementation.

Readings and resources

Capturing lessons learned:
www.thedigitalprojectmanager.com/project-management-lessons-learned-template/
Project acceptance templates:
www.projectmanagementdocs.com/project-closing-templates.html#axzz5PzJqdhif
Project monitoring and control:
www.bestpractices.ca.gov/project_management/monitoring.shtml
Project termination (managing the early termination of a project):
www.project-management-knowhow.com/project_termination.html
Status report templates:
www.projectconnections.com/knowhow/subsets/status-reports.html

Project templates

Template 4.I Project proposal

Project title	
Sponsor	
Proposed by	

1. **Background to the project:** [Briefly explain the context and the problem or opportunity that gives rise to the project]

2. **Goals and objectives;** [What is the project aiming to achieve?]

3. **Rationale:** [Why should these goals be pursued through a project?]

4. **Scope:** [Briefly state the boundaries of the project, i.e., what is included and what is excluded.]

5. **Deliverables:** [What will this project produce?]

6. **Stakeholders:** [Who has power and influence, who will be directly affected by the project? What are their concerns likely to be?]

7. **Timeframe and resourcing estimates:** [What is the likely duration of the project? What at the likely types and amounts of resources (labour and non-labour) required? What is the likely source of funding?]

8. **Risks and key assumptions:** [Identify all known major risks the project faces, and outline the major assumptions that may affect the project's viability or success.]

Signatures		Date
Proposer		
Sponsor		

Template 5.1 Project status report

Project status report for period ending: /   /

Project summary

Project name	
Sponsor	
Approved budget	
Actual start date	
Forecast end date	
Project manager	
Current phase	I.e., Initiation, planning, implementation, closure, review
Current status	I.e., Green, Amber or Red*

* Indicator definitions: Green = as planned, Amber = signs of trouble, Red = in trouble.

Progress

Project phases and activities	% Complete	Planned start date	Actual start date	Planned end date	Actual end date

Key accomplishments last period:

Upcoming tasks for this period:

Project financials <financial year>

Cost item	Approved budget $	Actual $	Forecast overrun $	Comment

Key project issues

Issue no.	Issue	Management

Key project risks

Risk no.	Risk	Mitigation

Change requests

Change request	Change description	Impact

Key communications / Planned events

Date	Description

Template 6.1 Process evaluation plan

Strategy	Key activities/ components	Indicators	Sources for measurement	When to be collected?	Who is responsible?

Template 6.2 Impact evaluation plan

Objective	Success indicators	Methods for measurement	When to be collected?	Who will be responsible?	Who will be involved?

Template 9.1 Change request form

1. Project information			
Submission date:		Reference:	
Initiating party:			
Project description:			

2. Change scope	
Description of change required:	
Justification:	

3. Project impacts	
Schedule/time:	
Cost:	
Other:	
Priority:	
On approval by all parties, the required change/s will be subject to quotation/ confirmation of cost	

4. Project status and currency	
Implementation details:	
Current phase:	
Implementation completion date:	

5. Approvals and signatures				
Project manager:		Approved	Yes/No	Date
Project sponsor:		Approved	Yes/No	Date

Template 9.2 Project acceptance

Project	
Sponsor/Client	
Submitted by:	
Submitted to:	
Date:	

Deliverable description	
	[Provide a brief description of the milestone and deliverables, and any necessary comments.]

☐	Project accepted	The Sponsor/Client agrees that the project deliverables have satisfied the acceptance criteria, and takes possession of the delivered product.

Approval signatures			
Name	Title	Signature	Date

Template 9.3 Final report

> **COVER**
> **Organisation name and logo**
> **Name of project**
> **Date of submission**

Contents page

Executive summary

- [ ] Maximum 2–3 pages giving an overview of project background, goals, methods, outcomes, achievements, recommendations or future implications

Introduction

- [ ] Project background and purpose, the problem statement or opportunity, acknowledgements of those who made significant contributions

Project goals and methods

- [ ] Drawn from the project plan—goals, objectives, scope, strategies, program
- [ ] Budget, resourcing, sponsor, team, project organisation, committee, etc.

Outcomes and key achievements

- [ ] Using the results of the impact evaluation

Issues

- [ ] Arising from the project but not resolved by it

Learning from the project

- [ ] A brief review of the results of the process evaluation

Recommendations and action

- [ ] Covering acceptance, handover, further monitoring and assessment of longer-term outcomes or realisation of intended benefits

References

- [ ] Published sources of evidence and internal documents cited in the report

Appendices (if needed)

- [ ] Key project documents
- [ ] Details of important project data and performance indicators not included in the body of the report

References

Alexander M., 2018, 'Agile project management: A comprehensive guide', www. cio.com/article/3156998/agile-development/agile-project-management-a-beginners-guide.html, accessed 28 June 2018

Alsène, É., 1999, 'Internal changes and project management structures within enterprises', *International Journal of Project Management*, vol. 17, no. 6, pp. 367–76

Andersen, E.S., Birchall, D., Jessen, S.A. & Money, A.H., 2006, 'Exploring project success', *Baltic Journal of Management*, vol. 1, no. 2, pp. 127–47

Andersen, E.S. & Jessen, S.A., 2003, 'Project maturity in organisations', *International Journal of Project Management*, vol. 21, no. 6, pp. 457–61

Assudani, R. & Kloppenborg, T.J., 2010, 'Managing stakeholders for project management success: An emergent model of stakeholders', *Journal of General Management*, vol. 35, no. 3, pp. 67–80

Atkinson, R., 1999, 'Project management: Cost, time and quality, two best guesses and a phenomenon, it's time to accept other success criteria', *International Journal of Project Management*, vol. 17, no. 6, pp. 337–42

Australian Digital Health Agency, 2018, 'About the agency', www.digitalhealth. gov.au/about-the-agency, accessed 29th May 2018

Australian National Audit Office. 2012, *Administration of the Gateway Review Process*, Canberra: Commonwealth Government of Australia

Aveyard, H., 2010, *Doing a Literature Review in Health and Social Care: A practical guide*, London: Open University Press

Axelos, 2017, *Managing Successful Projects with PRINCE2*, London: The Stationery Office

Belassi, W. & Tukel, O., 1996, 'A new framework for determining critical success/ failure factors in projects', *International Journal of Project Management*, vol. 14, no. 3, pp. 141–51

Berkun, S., 2008, *Making Things Happen: Mastering project management*, Sebastopol, CA: O'Reilly Media, Inc

Better Care Victoria, 2017, *Capability for Innovation and Improvement Strategy 2017–20*, www.bettercare.vic.gov.au/NewsAndEvents/News/Capabilitystrategy, accessed 25 July 2018

Bolles, D.L. & Hubbard, D.G., 2012, *A Compendium of PMO Case Studies: Reflecting project business management concepts*, Holland, MI: PBM concepts

Bradshaw, J.R., 1972a, 'The concept of social need', *New Society*, vol. 496, pp. 640–3

—1972b, 'The taxonomy of social need', in G. McLachlan (ed), *Problems and Progress in Medical Care*, Oxford: Oxford University Press, pp. 71–84

Carter, R. & Harris, A., 'Evaluation of health services' in G. Mooney & R. Scotton (eds), 1998, *Economics and Australian Health Policy*, Sydney: Allen & Unwin, pp. 154–71

Case, R., 1998, 'The structure of high-performing project management organisations', *Drug Information Journal*, vol. 32, no. 3, pp. 577–607

Chen, H.L., 2011, 'Predictors of project performance and the likelihood of project success', *Journal of International Management Studies*, vol. 6, no. 2, pp. 101–10

Chen, H.T., 1990, *Theory-driven evaluations*, Thousand Oaks, CA: SAGE Publications

Cleland, D.I. & Gareis, R., 2006, *Global Project Management Handbook*, New York, NY: McGraw-Hill Professional

Cleland, D.I. & King, W.R., 2008, *Project Management Handbook*, 2nd edn, West Sussex: John Wiley & Sons

Cookson, R., 2005, 'Evidence-based policy making in health care: What it is and what it isn't', *Journal of Health Service Research & Policy*, vol. 10, no. 2, pp. 118–21

Consumers Health Forum of Australia, 2017, *Review of the Consumer Representative Program: Executive summary and recommendations*, https://chf.org.au/sites/default/files/review_of_chf_crp_-_exec_summary_and_recs.pdf, accessed 14 June 2018

Courtney, M. & Briggs D.S., 2004, *Health Care Financial Management*, Sydney: Elsevier

Cousins, J.B., Goh, S.C., Elliot, C.J. & Bourgeois, I., 2014, 'Framing the capacity to do and use evaluation', in J.B. Cousins & I. Bourgeois (eds), *Organizational Capacity to Do and Use Evaluation: New directions*, Number 141, pp. 7–23

Day, G.E., Visawasm, G. & Briggs, D.S., 2004, 'The budget and financial control', in M. Courtney & D.S. Briggs (eds), *Health Care Financial Management*, Sydney: Elsevier, pp. 174–90

de Araújo, M.C.B., Alencar L.H. & de Miranda Mota C.M., 2017, 'Project procurement management: A structured literature review', *International Journal of Project Management*, vol. 35, no. 3, pp. 353–77

DeFillippi, R.J., 2001, 'Introduction: Project-based learning reflective practices and learning outcomes', *Management Learning*, vol. 32, no. 1, pp. 5–10

Department of Industry, Science and Resources, 2000, *Shaping Australia's Future: Innovation–framework paper*, Canberra: Commonwealth Government of Australia

Department of Treasury and Finance, 2017, *Investment Management Standard 2017*, www.dtf.vic.gov.au/infrastructure-investment/investment-management-standard, accessed 28 June 2018

Dobers, P. & Söderholm, A., 2009, 'Translation and inscription in development projects: Understanding environmental and health care-related organizational change', *Journal of Organizational Change Management*, vol. 22, no. 5, pp. 480–93

Dobie, C., 2007, *A Handbook of Project Management: A complete guide for beginners to professionals*, Sydney: Allen & Unwin

Drummond, M.F., Sculpher, M.J., Torrance, G.W., O'Brien, B.J. & Stoddart, G.L., 2015, *Methods for the Economic Evaluation of Health Care Programmes*, 4th edn, New York, NY: Oxford University Press

Eagar, K., Garrett, P. & Lin, V., 2001, *Health Planning: Australian perspectives*, Sydney: Allen & Unwin

Edmondson, A., 1999, 'Psychological safety and learning behavior in work teams', *Administrative Science Quarterly*, vol. 44, no. 2, pp. 350–83

Egan, G., 1994, *Working the Shadow Side: A guide to positive behind-the-scenes management*, San Francisco, CA: Jossey-Bass

Engwell, M., 2003, 'No project is an island: Linking projects to history and context', *Research Policy*, vol. 32, no. 5, pp. 789–808

Eskerod, P. & Huemann, M., 2013, 'Sustainable development and project stakeholder management: What standards say', *International Journal of Managing Projects in Business*, vol. 6, no. 1, pp. 36–50

Fink, A., 2010, *Conducting Research Literature Reviews: From the internet to paper*, 3rd edn, Los Angeles, CA: SAGE Publications

Fortune, J. & White, D., 2006, 'Framing of project critical success factors by a system model', *International Journal of Project Management*, vol. 24, no. 1, pp. 53–65

Gleeson, D., Dwyer, J., Lin, V., Legge, D. & Hughes, A., 2016, 'Can learning sets help policy managers with their wicked problems?', *Health Services Management Research,* vol. 29, no. 1/2, pp. 2–9

Goldratt, E.M., 1994, *It's Not Luck*, Great Barrington, MA: North River Press

Gomes, J., Romão, M. & Carvalho, H., 2016, 'Successful IS/IT projects in healthcare: Pretesting a questionnaire', *Procedia Computer Science*, vol. 100, pp. 375–82

Gray, A.M. & Wilkinson, T., 2016, 'Economic evaluation of healthcare interventions: Old and new directions', *Oxford Review of Economic Policy*, vol. 32, no. 1, pp. 102–21

Griffith, K. & Strasser, P.B., 2010, 'Integrating primary care with occupational health services: A success story', *AAOHN Journal*, vol. 58, no. 12, pp. 519–24

Hamilton, R.L., 1964, *Study of Methods for Evaluation of the PERT/Cost Management System*, Bedford, MA: The Mitre Corporation

Hassan, M.M., Bashir, S. & Abbas, S.M., 2017, 'The impact of project managers' personality on project success in NGOs: The mediating role of transformational leadership', *Project Management Journal*, vol. 48, no. 2, pp. 74–87

Haugan, G.T., 2003, *The Work Breakdown Structure in Government Contracting*, Vienna: Management Concepts

Hawe, P., Degeling, D. & Hall, J., 1990, *Evaluating Health Promotion: A health worker's guide*, Sydney: Maclennan and Petty

Hayes, H.B. & Miller, J., 2002, 'Using earned-value analysis for better project management', *Biopharm*, vol. 15, no. 3, pp. 58–60

Head, B.W., 2010, 'Reconsidering evidence-based policy: Key issues and challenges', *Policy and Society*, vol. 29, no. 2, pp. 77–94

Heagney, J., 2016, *Fundamentals of Project Management*, 5th edn, New York, NY: AMACOM

Health Issues Centre, 2018, *Guide to Consumer Engagement*, www.healthissuescentre.org.au/health-services/consumer-engagement-guide/, accessed 14 June 2018

Hill, G.M., 2010, *The Complete Project Management Methodology and Toolkit*, Boca Raton, FL: CRC Press

Hobbs, B. & Aubry, M., 2007, 'A multi-phase research program investigating project management offices (PMOs): The results of phase 1', *Project Management Journal*, vol. 38, no.1, pp. 74–86

Hodgson, D.E., 2004, 'Project work: The legacy of bureaucratic control in the post-bureaucratic organization', *Organization*, vol. 11, no. 1, pp. 81–100

Johnson, J., 2010, *Get a GRPI on Six Sigma Teams*, ISixSigma, www.isixsigma.com/implementation/getting-started-implementation/get-grpi-six-sigma-teams/, accessed 19 February 2019

Johnstone, L.P., Dwyer, J. & Lloyd, P.J., 2006, 'Leading and managing change', in M.G. Harris (ed), *Managing Health Services: Concepts and practice*, 2nd edn, Sydney: Elsevier, pp. 159–80

Keil, M., Mann, J. & Rai, A., 2000, 'Why software projects escalate: An empirical analysis and test of four theoretical models', *MIS Quarterly*, vol. 24, no. 4, pp. 631–64

Kerzner, H., 2009, *Project Management: A systems approach to planning, scheduling, and controlling*, 10th edn, Hoboken, NJ: John Wiley & Sons

Kerzner, H., 2017, *Project Management Case Studies*, 5th edn, Hoboken, NJ: John Wiley & Sons

Kliem, R.L., 2007, *Effective Communications for Project Management*, Boca Raton, FL: Auerbach Publications

Kliem, R.L., Ludin, I.S. & Robertson, K.L., 1997, *Project Management Methodology: A practical guide for the next millennium*, New York, NY: Marcel Dekker Inc

Kloppenborg, T.J., 2009, *Contemporary Project Management: Organize, plan, perform*, Mason, OH: South-Western Cengage Learning

Kovner, A. & Rundall, T.G., 2006, 'Evidence-based management reconsidered', *Frontiers of Health Services Management*, vol. 22, no. 3, pp. 3–22

Kovacevic, M., Jovicic, M., Djapan, M. & Zivanovic-Makuzic, I., 2016, 'Lean thinking in health care: Review of implementation results', *International Journal for Quality Research*, vol. 10, no. 1, pp. 219–30

Kovacevic, M., Odeleye, O.E., Sietsema, W.K., Schwarz, K.M. & Torchio, C.R., 2001, 'Financial concepts to conducting and managing clinical trials within budget', *Therapeutic Innovation and Regulatory Science*, vol. 35, no. 3, pp. 1031–38

Lao Tse, 1963, *Tao Te Ching: The way of virtue* (trans by Patrick M. Byrne), New York, NY: SquareOne Classics

Larsen, L., Cummins, J., Brown, H., Ajmal, T., Beers, H. & Lee, J., 2005, *Learning from Evaluation: Summary of reports of evaluations of leadership initiatives*, London: Office for Public Management/NHS Leadership Centre

Lavis, J., Davies, H., Oxman, A., Denis, J., Golden-Biddle, K. & Ferlie, E., 2005, 'Towards systematic reviews that inform health care management and policy-making', *Journal of Health Services Research & Policy*, vol. 10, suppl. 1, pp. 35–48

Latham, G.P. & Locke, E.A., 1979, 'Goal-setting: A motivational technique that works', *Organizational Dynamics*, vol. 8, no. 2, pp. 68–80

Leggat, S., Balding, C. & Anderson, J., 2011, 'Empowering health-care managers in Australia: An action learning approach', *Health Services Management Research*, vol. 24, no. 4, pp. 196–202

Leggat, S. & Dwyer, J., 2005, 'Improving hospital performance: Culture change is not the answer', *Healthcare Quarterly*, vol. 8, no. 2, pp. 60–6

Legge, D., Stanton, P. & Smyth, A., 2006, 'Learning management (and managing your own learning)', in M.G. Harris (ed), *Managing Health Services: Concepts and practice*, 2nd edn, Sydney: Elsevier, pp. 1–24

Levasseur, R.E., 2010, 'People skills: Ensuring project success—a change management perspective', *Interfaces*, vol. 40, no. 2, pp. 159–62

Lewin, K., 1958, 'Group decisions and social change', in E.E. Maccoby (ed), *Readings in Social Psychology*, New York, NY: Holt, Rinehart & Winston, pp. 192–211

Liang, Z. & Howard, P.F., 2011, 'Evidence-informed managerial decision-making—what evidence counts? (part two)', *Asia Pacific Journal of Health Management*, vol. 6, no. 2, pp. 12–21

Liang, Z., Howard, P.F. & Rasa, J., 2011, 'Evidence-informed managerial decision-making—what evidence counts? (part one)', *Asia Pacific Journal of Health Management*, vol. 6 no. 1, pp. 23–9

Lock, D., 2007, *The Essentials of Project Management*, Burlington, VT: Gower Publishing Company

Longest, B.B., 2004, *Managing Health Programs and Projects*, San Francisco, CA: Jossey-Bass

Lundy, V. & Morin, P.P., 2013, 'Project leadership influences resistance to change: The case of the Canadian Public Service', *Project Management Journal*, vol. 44, no. 4, pp. 45–64

Martens, M.L. & Carvalho, M.M., 2016, 'Sustainability and success variables in the project management context: An expert panel', *Project Management Journal*, vol. 47, no. 6, pp. 24–43

Martin, V., 2002, *Managing Projects in Health and Social Care*, New York, NY: Routledge

Martin, V. & Henderson, E., 2001, *Managing in Health and Social Care*, London: Routledge

McDavid, J.C. & Hawthorn, L.R.L., 2006, *Program Evaluation & Performance Measurement: An introduction to practice*, London: SAGE Publications

McElroy, W., 1996, 'Implementing strategic change through projects', *International Journal of Project Management*, vol. 14, no. 6, pp. 325–9

Meacock, R., Kristensen, S.R. & Sutton, M., 2014, 'Paying for improvements in quality: Recent experience in the NHS in England', *Nordic Journal of Health Economics*, vol. 2, no.1, pp. 239–55

Meredith, J.R. & Mantel, S.J 2012, *Project Management: A managerial approach*, 8th edn, Hoboken, NJ: John Wiley & Sons

Mintzberg, H., 1991, 'Ideology and the missionary organization', in H. Mintzberg & J.B. Quinn (eds), *The Strategy Process: Concepts, contexts, cases,* Englewood Cliffs, NJ: Prentice-Hall, pp. 352–8

Mishra, P., Dangayach, G.S. & Mittal, M.L., 2011, 'An empirical study on identification of critical success factors in project based organizations', *Global Business and Management Research*, vol. 3, no. 3&4, pp. 356–68

Muennig, P., 2002, *designing and Conducting Cost-Effectiveness Analysis in Medicine and Health Care*, San Francisco, CA: Jossey-Bass

Mukund, 2017, *Why a Feasibility Study is Important in Project Management*, www. simplilearn.com/feasibility-study-article, accessed 28 June 2018

Newton, R., 2012, *Project Management Step by Step: How to plan and manage a highly successful project*, Harlow: Pearson

NHS Institute for Innovation and Improvement, 2008, 'Quality and service improvement tools: Benefits realisation', www.institute.nhs.uk/quality_and_ service_improvement_tools/quality_and_service_improvement_tools/ benefits_realisation.html, accessed 3 September 2012

NSW Government, 2018, *Benefits Realisation Management Framework*, Sydney: NSW Government Finance Service and Innovation

O'Kelly, S.W. & Maxwell, R., 2001, 'Implementing clinical governance: Medical training should include project management', *British Medical Journal*, vol. 323, no. 7315, pp. 753

Olsen, R.P., 1971, 'Can project management be defined?', *Project Management Quarterly*, vol. 2, no. 1, pp. 12–14

Osei-Kyei, R. & Chan, A.P.C., 2017, 'Comparative analysis of the success criteria for public–private partnership projects in Ghana and Hong Kong', *Project Management Journal*, vol. 48, no. 4, pp. 80–92

Parliamentary Office of Science and Technology, 2003, *Government IT Projects, Report 200*, POST, London, www.parliament.uk/documents/post/pr200.pdf, accessed 19 February 2019

Partington, D., 1996, 'The project management of organizational change', *International Journal of Project Management*, vol. 14, no. 1, pp. 13–21

Patton, M.Q., 2008, *Utilization-Focused Evaluation*, 4th edn, Thousand Oaks, CA: SAGE Publications

Patton, M.Q., 1990, *Qualitative Evaluation and Research Methods*, Thousand Oaks, CA: SAGE Publications

Pawson, R. & Tilley, N., 1997, *Realistic Evaluation*, London: SAGE Publications

Pinto, J.K., 2000, 'Understanding the role of politics in successful project management', *International Journal of Project Management*, vol. 18, no. 2, pp. 85–91

Pinto, J.K. & Slevin, D.P., 1988, 'Critical success factors across the project life cycle: Definitions and measurement techniques', *Project Management Journal*, vol. 19, no. 3, pp. 67–75

Piperca, S. & Floricel, S., 2012, 'A typology of unexpected events in complex projects', *International Journal of Managing Projects in Business*, vol. 5, no. 2, pp. 248–65

Project Management Institute, 2017, *A Guide to the Project Management Body of Knowledge (PMBOK® Guide)*, 6th edn, Newtown Square, PA: PMI Inc

Proudlove, N.C., Gordon, K. & Boaden, R., 2003, 'Can good bed management solve the overcrowding in accident and emergency departments?', *Emergency Medicine Journal*, vol. 20, no. 2, pp. 149–55

Roberts, P., 2011, *Effective Project Management*, London: Kogan Page

Rosacker, K., Zuckweiler, K.M. & Buelow, J.R., 2010, 'An empirical evaluation of hospital project implementation success', *Academy of Health Care Management Journal*, vol. 6, no. 1, pp. 37–53

Rosenau, M.D. & Githens, G.D., 2005, *Successful Project Management: A step by step approach with practical examples*, 4th edn, Hoboken, NJ: John Wiley & Sons

Roughley, A., 2009, *Developing and Using Program Logic in Natural Resource Management: User guide*, Canberra: Commonwealth Government of Australia

Rowe, S.F. & Sikes, S., 2006, 'Lessons learned: Taking it to the next level', paper presented at PMI® Global Congress 2006—North America, Seattle, WA, NewtownSquare, PA: PMI Inc, www.pmi.org/learning/library/lessons-learned-next-level-communicating-7991

Royse, D., Staton-Tindall, M., Badger, K. & Webster, J.M., 2009, *Needs Assessment Pocket Guide to Social Work Research Methods*, New York, NY: Oxford University Press

Royse, D., Thyer, B.A., Padgett, D.K. & Logan, T.K., 2006, *Program Evaluations: An introduction*, 4th edn, Belmont, CA: Thomson Brooks/Cole

Rubin, I.M., Plovnick, M.S. & Fry, R.E., 1977, *Task Oriented Team Development*, New York, NY: McGraw-Hill

Rummler, C.A. & Brache, A.P., 1995, *Improving Performance: How to manage the white space on the organization chart*, San Francisco, CA: Jossey-Bass

Ryan, R. & Hill, S., 2016, 'How to grade the quality of the evidence', Cochrane Consumers and Communication Group, http://cccrg.cochrane.org/author-resources, accessed 29 June 2018

Saunders, R.P., Evans, M.H. & Joshi, P., 2005. 'Developing a process-evaluation plan for assessing health promotion program implementation: A how-to guide', *Health Promotion Practice*, vol. 6, no. 2, pp. 134–47

Shao, J., Müller, R. & Turner, J.R., 2012, 'Measuring program success', *Project Management Journal*, vol. 43, no. 1, pp. 37–49

Shokri-Ghasabeh, M. & Kavousi-Chabok, K., 2009, 'Generic project success and project management success criteria and factors: Literature review and survey', *World Scientific and Engineering Academy and Society Transactions on Business and Economics*, vol. 6, no. 8, pp. 456–68

Shore, B., 2008, 'Systematic biases and culture in project failures', *Project Management Journal*, vol. 39, no. 4, pp. 5–16

Shortell, S.M., 2006, 'Promoting evidence-based management', *Frontiers of Health Services Management*, vol. 22 no. 3, pp. 23–9

Sie, B.S. & Liang, Z., 2015, 'Australian postgraduate programs in health service management—the joint efforts', SHAPE Symposium, Sydney

Simpson, S. & DuPlessis, S., 2015, *More About Unwritten Ground Rules*, UGRS, www.ugrs.net/more-about-ugrs, accessed 28 December 2015

Singaram, M. & Jain, P., 2018, 'What is the difference between proof of concept and prototype?', www.entrepreneur.com/article/307454, accessed 28 June 2018

Smartsheet, 2018, *Eight Elements of an Effective Change Process*, www.smartsheet.com/8-elements-effective-change-management-process, accessed 29 June 2018

South Australian Community Health Research Unit (SACHRU), 2008, 'Planning and evaluation wizard', Flinders University, Adelaide, www.flinders.edu.au/medicine/sites/pew/pew_home.cfm, accessed 19 February 2019

Stace, D. & Dunphy, D., 2001, *Beyond the Boundaries: Leading and recreating the successful enterprise*, 2nd edn, Sydney: McGraw-Hill

Stacey, R.D., 2001, *Strategic Management and Organizational Dynamics*, 3rd edn, London: Pitman

Swiatek, P.R., Chung, K.C. & Mahmoudi, E., 2016, 'Surgery and research: A practical approach to managing the research process', *Plastic and Reconstructive Surgery*, vol. 137, no. 1, p. 361–6

Tabassi, A.A., Roufechaei, K.M., Abu Bakar, A.H. & Yusof, N. 2017, 'Linking team condition and team performance: A transformational leadership approach', *Project Management Journal,* vol. 48, no. 2, pp. 22–38

Taylor, J., 2004, *Managing Information Technology Projects: Applying project management strategies to software, hardware, and integration initiatives*, New York, NY: American Management Association

Taylor-Powell, E., Jones, L. & Henert, E., 2002, *Enhancing Program Performance with Logic Models*, https://lmcourse.ces.uwex.edu/, accessed 30 September 2018

Turner, R., 2007, *Gower Handbook of Project Management,* 4th edn, Burlington, VT, Gower Publishing Limited

Van Horne, J., 1998, *Financial Management and Policy*, 11th edn, Upper Saddle River, NJ: Prentice Hall

Verzuh, E., 2012, *The Fast Forward MBA in Project Management*, 5th edn, Hoboken, NJ: John Wiley & Sons

Victorian Ombudsman, 2011, *Investigation into ICT-enabled Projects*, Melbourne: Victorian Ombudsman

Victoria State Government, Department of Treasury and Finance 2018, *Project Assurance Reviews* www.dtf.vic.gov.au/gateway-review-process/project-assurance-reviews, accessed 19 February 2019

Wadsworth, Y., 2010, *Building in Research and Evaluation: Human inquiry for living systems*, Sydney: Action Research Press, Hawthorn and Allen & Unwin

Westland, J., 2018, 'What is post-implementation review in project management?', www.projectmanager.com/blog/post-implementation-review, accessed 12 September 2018

Westerveld, E., 2003, 'The project excellence model: Linking success criteria and critical success factors', *International Journal of Project Management*, vol. 21, no. 6, pp. 411–18

Westland, J., 2006, *The Project Management Life Cycle: A complete step-by-step methodology for initiating, planning, executing & closing a project successfully*, London: Kogan Page

White, D. & Fortune, J., 2002, 'Current practice in project management: An empirical study', *International Journal of Project Management,* vol. 20, no. 1, pp. 1–11

Wikipedia, 2018a, 'Organizational change fatigue', https://en.wikipedia.org/wiki/Organizational_change_fatigue, accessed 28 August 2018

—2018b, 'Project assurance', https://en.wikipedia.org/wiki/Project_assurance, accessed 29 June 2018

—2018c, 'Project management office', https://en.wikipedia.org/wiki/Project_management_office, accessed 28 August 2018

—2018d, 'Systems development life cycle', https://en.wikipedia.org/wiki/Systems_development_life_cycle, accessed 19 February 2019

Williams, T., 2015, 'Identifying success factors in construction projects: A case study', *Project Management Journal*, vol. 47, no. 1, pp. 97–112

Willis, C.D., Saul, J., Bevan, H., Scheirer, M.A., Best, A., Greenhalgh, T., Mannion, R., Cornelissen, E., Howland, D., Jenkins, E. & Bitz, J., 2016, 'Sustaining organizational culture change in health systems', *Journal of Health Organization and Management*, vol. 30, no. 1, pp. 2–30

Yalegama, S., Chileshe, N. & Ma, T., 2016, 'Critical success factors for community-driven development projects: A Sri Lankan community perspective', *International Journal of Project Management*, vol. 34, no. 4, pp. 643–59

Yazici, H.J., 2009, 'The role of project management maturity and organizational culture in perceived performance', *Project Management Journal*, vol. 40, no. 3, pp. 14–33

Yeow, J. & Edler, J., 2012, 'Innovation procurement as projects', *Journal of Public Procurement*, vol. 12, no. 4, pp. 472–504

Zuo, J., Zillante, G., Zhao, Z.Y. & Xia, B., 2014, 'Does project culture matter? A comparative study of two major hospital projects', *Facilities*, vol. 32, no. 13/14, pp. 801–24

Index